THE ORIGIN OF RADAR

As Director of Research at the United States Naval Laboratory, Washington, D.C., and holder of forty patents in the development of radar, ROBERT MORRIS PAGE is in a commanding position to tell the story of what may have been the most valuable weapon of World War II and certainly is one of the outstanding technological achievements of the mid-twentieth century. He worked on pulsed radar from its very beginning, and in this book, by setting the record straight on who discovered what and when, he makes a significant contribution to a controversial chapter in the history of science.

The author was born on June 2, 1903, son of a Methodist clergyman, and spent his boyhood on a farm near Minneapolis, Minnesota. After attending a one-room (but not red) rural school and a Minneapolis high school, he entered Hamline University, in St. Paul, to study for the ministry. Building radio receivers had been his hobby in high school days, and at Hamline, under the influence of a talented and

2

understanding physics teacher, he decided on a career in science. After passing a Civil Service examination, he accepted an appointment to the Naval Research Laboratory in 1927 and devoted his professional life to its projects. Precision instrumentation in electronics was his speciality until he became research administrator.

In 1934 Dr. Page completed the world's first pulse radar for the detection of aircraft. In recognition of this and his other achievements many honors have come his way. He received the President's Award for Distinguished Federal Civilian Service on March 8, 1960; the Wheaton College Centennial Award, in January 1960; the Captain Robert Dexter Conrad Award of the Navy in 1959; the Franklin Institute's Stuart Ballantine Medal, in 1957; the Harry Diamond Memorial Award of the Institute of Radio Engineers, in 1953; the Presidential Certificate of Merit, in 1946; the Navy's Distinguished Civilian Service Award, in 1945, and the Certificate of Award of the Office of Scientific Research and Development, 1945. Dr. Page regards these awards as "bearing testimony to a highly competent and loyally devoted group of research engineers in a Laboratory that has had an unusually prolific record of scientific achievement."

Dr. Page is a Fellow of the Institute of Radio Engineers, the American Association for the Advancement of Science and the American Scientific Affiliation and a member of the Scientific Research Society of America, and the Armed Forces Electronics & Communications Association. He was chairman of the Washington section of the I.R.E. in 1958–59 and a member of the I.R.E. Board of Editors, 1946–53.

He has contributed technical papers to the *Proceedings of the I.R.E.*, the *Journal of the Washington Academy of Sciences* and the *Journal of the Society for Personal Administration,* and is the author of "A Conclusive Test," in *Evidence of God in an Expanding Universe* (G. P. Putnam's Sons, 1958), and of a section in *Airborne Radar* (D. Van Nostrand, 1961). He has an M.S. degree from George Washington University, in Washington, and an honorary D.Sc. from Hamline.

In college Dr. Page's rival in scholarship was Miss Signe Benson, who finished her undergraduate course with the highest record in the seventy-five-year history of Hamline. Unable to beat her, Dr. Page decided to join her, and they were married in 1928. The Pages have two sons and a daughter and make their home in Washington.

The Origin of
RADAR

BY ROBERT MORRIS PAGE

SCIENCE
STUDY
SERIES
o

Published by Anchor Books
Doubleday & Company, Inc.
Garden City, New York
1962

ILLUSTRATIONS BY KENNETH CROOK

THE SCIENCE STUDY SERIES

The Science Study Series offers to students and to the general public the writing of distinguished authors on the most stirring and fundamental topics of science, from the smallest known particles to the whole universe. Some of the books tell of the role of science in the world of man, his technology and civilization. Others are biographical in nature, telling the fascinating stories of the great discoverers and their discoveries. All the authors have been selected both for expertness in the fields they discuss and for ability to communicate their special knowledge and their own views in an interesting way. The primary purpose of these books is to provide a survey within the grasp of the young student or the layman. Many of the books, it is hoped, will encourage the reader to make his own investigations of natural phenomena.

The Series, which now offers topics in all the sciences and their applications, had its beginning in a project to revise the secondary schools' physics curriculum. At the Massachusetts Institute of Technology during 1956 a group of physicists, high school teachers, journalists, apparatus designers, film producers, and other specialists organized the Physical Science Study Committee, now operating as a part of Educational Services Incorporated, Watertown, Massachusetts. They pooled their knowledge and experience toward the design and creation of aids to the learning of physics. Initially their effort was supported by the National Science Foundation, which has continued to aid the program. The Ford Foundation, the Fund for the Advancement of Education, and the Alfred P. Sloan Foundation have also given support. The Committee has created a textbook, an extensive film series, a laboratory guide, especially designed apparatus, and a teacher's source book.

The Series is guided by a Board of Editors, consisting of Bruce F. Kingsbury, Managing Editor; John H. Durston, General Editor; Paul F. Brandwein, the Conservation Foundation and Harcourt, Brace & World, Inc.; Francis L. Friedman, Massachusetts Institute of Technology; Samuel A. Goudsmit, Brookhaven National Laboratory; Philippe LeCorbeiller, Harvard University; and Gerard Piel, *Scientific American.*

CONTENTS

CONTENTS

10

THE ORIGIN OF RADAR

CHAPTER 1

THE DISCOVERY OF RADAR

From mythology we learn that Aladdin had a magic lamp that served as a sort of call box for a Genie who worked wonders on command. We also learn that Pandora had a magic box held shut with a knot tied so tight that it was very difficult to untie, but Pandora kept at it until she got the box open. What then came out could never be put back, though it cursed all mankind. Now if I were to tell you about a pair of magic spectacles that would increase your range of vision by a hundredfold, enabling you to see right through clouds and darkness; giving you a living map of everything around you for a hundred miles, showing roads, mountains, storm centers, and moving airplanes; enabling you to determine precisely the distances to the sun and nearby planets, the exact shape of the earth: if I were to say that the secret of the magic spectacles would be used in inventions enabling ships and aircraft to fix instantly their exact locations over the earth, would give rise to new communication systems, would automatize industrial

13

processes with unheard-of precision, would multiply a hundred million times the power of mathematics in research, and enable machines to make logical decisions with almost infinite speed and accuracy— if I were to assert all these accomplishments, or even half of them, you would be sure I was trying to outdo both Aladdin and Pandora. But it is no myth that radar is that pair of magic spectacles, and no myth that the short-pulse techniques originally developed for radar have been applied to world-wide navigation, coded pulse modulation for communication and telemetry, digital automation and computation, and digital logic and learning machines, all representing enormous advances in precision, speed, and versatility.

One would think that so important a contribution to the world's technology would be chronicled with great care at every step in its evolution, and that each person who significantly contributed to its origin would be meticulously identified with his gift for the benefit of all posterity. This, unfortunately, is not the case, and for reasons quite understandable. Radar was for many years a carefully guarded military secret, and many competitive interests became involved in its development and production before it was released for public information. When radar finally was made public property, those who started it had become more interested in developing other new things than in contending for the purification of history. As a result, the true origin of radar has become obscured in conflicting claims and "tales not-quite-agreed-upon." But before we try to set the record straight, it might be well to learn the secret of the magic spectacles.

How Radar Works

The name "radar" was coined from the words *RA*dio *D*etection *A*nd *R*anging by two U. S. Naval officers, F. R. Furth and S. M. Tucker. In the simplest terms, radar is a radio device for "seeing" remote objects, using radio waves instead of light waves, and when it "sees" an object, it indicates its position with uncanny accuracy. Radar does this by sending out, in a known direction, very short but powerful pulses of radio frequency energy spaced widely apart and receiving the weak pulses reflected back from objects or "targets" which the pulses have illuminated. The time required for the radio energy, or signal, to travel out to the target and back is measured, and the distance is indicated by the time of travel, since the greater the distance to the target, the greater the time required for the signal to get to the target and back again.

Sounds easy, doesn't it? Let's take a closer look. We send radio energy in a known direction with a directional antenna, that is, an antenna which forms a radio beam. The sharper the beam, the better we can measure direction. A really sharp beam like a searchlight beam would be ideal for some purposes. But the sharpness of the beam depends on the size of the antenna measured in wavelengths of the radio frequency. A large searchlight may be five feet across. But with a radio antenna even twenty feet across, it

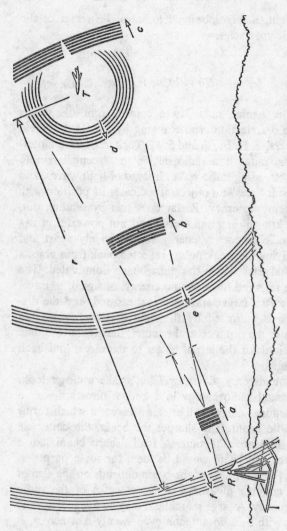

Fig. 1. A radar pulse is shown at various points in its trajectory as it moves out from the radar R to the target T, at a distance r, and back to the radar.

would require very short radio wavelengths to produce a sharp beam. Producing beams sharp enough for radar needs wavelengths much shorter, or frequencies much higher, than were in use when radar was first developed. It is also necessary to send out very high power pulses. The higher the frequency, the more difficult it is to produce high power. Radar requires pulses at a level of many thousands of watts, that is, many kilowatts. At the time of its first development the necessary frequencies had been produced at power levels of only a few watts, and even then only in laboratories. So a way had to be found to increase power a thousandfold. Still another problem is the extreme shortness of the pulses that have to be sent. Since radio waves travel at the velocity of light, which is 186,000 miles a second, the energy goes out to and back from a target a hundred miles away in a thousandth of a second (a millisecond). If one is to see targets only one mile away with radar, the pulses can be only a few millionths of a second (a few microseconds) long. To build up a radio signal to a power level of many kilowatts and then shut it off completely in a few microseconds was an unheard-of "stunt" at any radiofrequency when radar was first developed.

Then there is the problem (Fig. 1) of measuring time to a microsecond and time intervals of small fractions of a millisecond. And last but not least, there is the problem of receiving, amplifying, and displaying the tiny bits of energy reflected back from aircraft many miles away, while right beside the sensitive receiver is a transmitter sending out pulses of many kilowatts on the same frequency. And as if this were not difficult enough, the receiver with its extreme sensitivity to the tiniest signals shares the same antenna with the transmitter, whose tremendous pulse wallop can make sparks jump half an inch in air. Doesn't look so easy now, does it? In fact, in those far-off days it took nerve even to suggest the pulse method for radar, and more faith than a little to embark on a serious program to develop it. It is an interesting story which has never seen the light of popular publication, and so this telling becomes something of an event.

A straight record of any new development recognizes four main stages through which it evolves: discovery, idea, invention, and use. We shall now trace the origin of radar through these four stages. First we ask, how was radar discovered? And what is discovery anyway?

In scientific research, discovery is the uncovering of the secrets of nature. It may be done directly, by design, or indirectly, by accident. In the first case, something suspected is purposefully sought. For example, an observed perturbation in the orbit of the planet Neptune suggested the possibility of another planet not yet discovered. Calculations indicated where the unknown planet, if any, would have to be in order to cause the observed perturbation. Search with telescopes in the indicated region resulted in discovery of the planet Pluto. Discovery by design has the aspect of a treasure hunt and is just as much fun as the game itself.

In the second case, some quite unexpected observation may lead to a discovery unrelated to the object of the moment. Quite frequently the discovered phenomenon occurs as an interference with the desired result, or as a "failure" of an experiment. The normal reaction is to ignore it, or try to get rid of it. The ability to see in such "accidents" the possibility of unexpected discovery is the mark of a research scientist. Some people seem to have a propensity for making discoveries. Whether it is a persistence of good luck, a special providence, or the habit of inquiring into peripheral observations, a fortunate few have it in high degree. Such a propensity for accidental discovery is called "serendipity," from the three princes of Serendip who were so endowed. Whatever the mechanism, the importance of discoveries made in this way puts a high premium on being alert to the unexpected. For example, the "discoveries" which resulted in the development of radar were all of the "unexpected accident" type. But let's get on with the story. What were the discoveries, and how did they lead to the development of radar?

The "Beat" Method of Detection

We must go back to a little shack on the east side of the Anacostia River in Washington, D.C., known as the Aircraft Radio Laboratory, Anacostia Naval Air Station, and to a truck on the west side of the river near Hains Point. With a high frequency radio transmitter in the shack, and a radio receiver in the truck, A. H. Taylor and L. C. Young were studying high frequency radio communication. When they had obtained a steady tone they wanted, they heard the tone unexpectedly swell to nearly double its normal

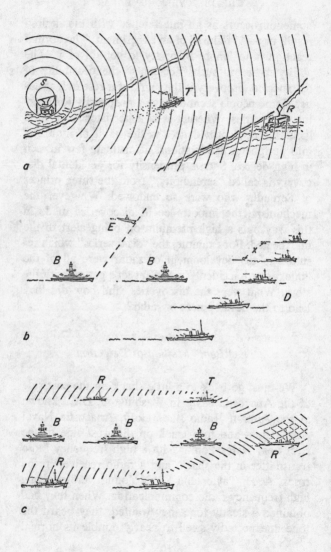

a

b

c

loudness, then die away to almost nothing. After a few moments, the process reversed. The tone swelled from almost nothing to nearly double normal loudness, then settled back to normal loudness, where it remained without further noted disturbance. This quite unexpected occurrence (Fig. 2) was observed to coincide with the passage of a river steamer across the line of sight between the transmitter and the receiver. Now Taylor and Young were research men. They were conducting an experiment in radio communication. The river steamer interfered with their experiment. They had to stand by and wait until the ship got out of the way before they could resume their work. But here another element enters. Taylor and Young were employed by the U. S. Navy. They had sailed on Navy ships and were thoroughly familiar with many Navy problems. They knew that one of the Navy's problems was to prevent enemy ships from penetrating harbors and fleet formations under cover of darkness. So when they observed how easily the passage of the river steamer was "detected" by radio, they proposed that radio be used in "burglar alarm" fashion across harbor entrances, and between ships operating in pairs, with transmitter on one ship and receiver on another, to detect the passage of any ship between the two at night or in fog. The proposal

---

FIG. 2. (a) First radar "discovery," in 1922. Ship, T, cuts off high frequency radio signal from transmitter, S, at receiver, R.

(b) Problem: To screen main fleet, B, from enemy, E, by destroyers, D, with range of visibility, X.

(c) Idea: Use radio transmitters at T, receivers at R, to increase range of visibility.

was made officially in a letter from the Commanding Officer, NAS, Anacostia, to the Navy Bureau of Engineering, dated September 27, 1922.

Having informed the Bureau of Engineering of their discovery and a possible Navy use of it, Taylor and Young proceeded to investigate further. It is easy to see why the signal should disappear when the ship got in the way since the receiver could not "see" the transmitter, but why should the signal get stronger just before and just after the cutoff? We explain this by thinking of the radio signal as a wave motion existing along the path from the transmitter to the receiver. The signal at the receiver is an oscillating signal, in which the voltage in the antenna is constantly swinging back and forth between positive and negative. As the ship approaches the signal path, some of the wave energy is reflected from the bow of the ship and reaches the receiver, but by a path slightly longer than the straight line path from transmitter to receiver. At the receiver these two waves add together. If they are in phase when they add together—that is, if both waves are going positive and negative at the same time—the received signal is increased to equal the sum of the two signals. However, if they arrive in antiphase—that is, if one wave is going negative while the other is going positive—they tend to cancel each other, and the resultant signal is decreased to equal the difference between the two signals. When the bow of the ship is far enough back from the straight line path so that the path length difference between the straight line and the reflected line is just one half wavelength, one would expect the two waves at the receiver to be in anti-phase and cancel out. But something strange happens when the wave is reflected. In the reflection the wave (Fig. 3) is "flipped over," and its phase is thereby reversed. Where it went positive before reflection, it goes negative afterward, and vice versa. Thus the phase reversal due to reflection and the phase reversal due to the extra half wavelength of travel distance just cancel, and the two waves add in phase at the receiver to increase the signal.

Now, to go back to Taylor and Young, when the ship came closer to the straight line path, the two paths became more nearly the same length, the phase reversal at reflection could not be canceled by the phase difference in path length, and the two waves started to cancel each other at the receiver. When the bow reached the straight line path, the two paths were equal and the two waves canceled at the receiver. When the ship crossed the straight line path, both waves were cut off, and remained off until the ship passed, and reflection from the stern added to the straight line path to increase the signal again.

If this explanation is correct, then there should be a position of the ship still farther removed where the path difference is a whole wavelength, and because of the phase reversal at reflection the two waves again should cancel at the receiver. This cancellation at the receiver should occur over and over as the ship moves farther and farther away through path length differences of successive multiples of whole wavelengths. In between the cancellations should occur strong signals when the path difference is an odd multiple of a half wavelength and the two waves add in phase at the receiver. When they investigated further, Taylor and Young found that these successively strong and

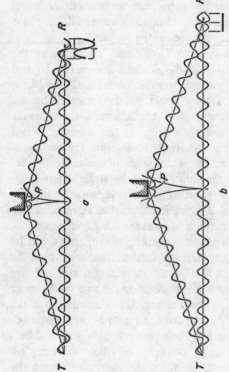

FIG. 3. A wave propagating through space will be "flipped over" or reversed in phase when reflected, as shown at points P. Also, the reflected path from T to P to R is longer than the direct path from T to R.
(a) Path difference plus phase reversal add to double signal at R.
(b) Path difference plus phase reversal cancel to give zero signal at R.

weak signals did in fact occur when ships approached or receded from the line of sight between transmitter and receiver. The detection of moving objects by observing the signal fluctuations in a radio receiver as the object moved through the radio propagation field became known as the "beat" method of radio detection.

Aircraft Detection

The next "accident" occurred in 1930, when the same Mr. Young and Mr. L. A. Hyland at the U. S. Naval Research Laboratory, successor to the Aircraft Radio Laboratory, were experimenting with short-wave direction finding. A short-wave transmitter emitting a steady tone from the main Laboratory was being received by a short-wave receiver several miles away. The receiver was using a special directive antenna that had a very narrow "blind spot" in one direction. The antenna was rotated to point the blind spot toward the transmitter so that the tone could scarcely be heard, thus indicating the direction to the transmitter. In the operation the tone mysteriously got loud and fluctuated violently. Hyland, who had charge of the receiver, checked and rechecked all the receiver parts trying to find the trouble. The tone soon became steady and quiet, but a little later began the same puzzling dance again. In exasperation Hyland was about to return to the Laboratory with his "balky" receiver when he observed a significant fact: every time the tone "danced" there was an airplane flying overhead. Realizing the importance of this "discovery," that an airplane can be detected by radio, he immediately returned to the Laboratory and wrote a memorandum describing his experience. This also was reported in a letter from the Director, NRL, to the Chief, Bureau of Engineering, dated November 5, 1930.

The 1922 radio detection work had been done as a part of the general research on high frequency radio. It established the "beat" method of detection of ships by radio. Hyland's observation resulted in formalization of a project which was immediately set up with the title Detection of Enemy Vessels and Aircraft by Radio. Under this project the beat method was successfully applied to the detection of aircraft. We shall refer to this again in Chapter 2.

These two "discoveries," one in 1922 and the other in 1930, were crucial events in the experience of Taylor and Young and led them to initiate later the original development of radar.

CHAPTER 2

THE RADAR IDEA

We come now to the second or "idea" phase of radar. What is meant here is not the many ideas that appear in the "invention" phase, but the basic ideas of how to attempt to attain the objective. To appreciate the importance of this phase, we need to understand the nature of ideas and what makes ideas significant. As with discovery, so with new ideas; they may be derived from logical manipulations of knowledge, or they may appear as if by accident, containing something more than existed in prior knowledge. This latter phenomenon may be difficult to prove objectively. My own experience, however, leaves me with no doubt of its reality. I think of such ideas as coming from some source outside myself, and therefore as true instances of inspiration. I will give an example later when I discuss the radar duplexer.

Whether a new idea is born of the purposeful treasure hunt or of inspiration, it is as much a discovery as the uncovering of a secret of nature. A few people seem to be endowed with a special propensity for

27

giving birth to ideas, and we say these people have the gift of great originality. Thus we may define originality as luck, special providence, or skill in the discovery of ideas.

I referred to ideas as being born. Is it not logical to ask if they may not also die? I think we might all agree that if an idea is born when it enters the conscious mind of man, then as far as the world is concerned, it dies when the man dies without putting it to use or communicating it to someone else. Ideas live, therefore, through being put to use or being communicated to others.

When Taylor and Young discovered the detection of moving ships by radio in 1922, they suggested to the Bureau of Engineering that high frequency transmitters and receivers be put on ships, so that any two vessels would be alerted by radio if a third passed between them. Since this alarm system would work in fog, smoke, and darkness, even when the two ships were many miles apart, it could be a valuable addition to Naval capability. This was an idea born of newly discovered knowledge and familiarity with an unsolved problem, and of the logical application of the one to the other. Had these men been unfamiliar with the problem of screening ships in the Navy, they would not have had that particular idea—but they may have had some other idea, depending upon their own backgrounds and experience. This particular idea was not radar, but it was the beginning of a long chain of events that ultimately led to radar.

The next link in that chain was forged when, in 1925, Drs. G. Breit and M. A. Tuve of the Department of Terrestrial Magnetism, Carnegie Institution of Washington, proposed the use of radio pulses for measuring the height of the ionosphere,* that well-known ceiling of ions floating 50 to 70 miles above the surface of the earth and constituting a reflector of medium and high frequency radio waves. The idea of measuring distance by timing the flight of pulses of radiant energy was not new. It had been done for years with sound waves, both in the air and under water. But sound waves take about two seconds to echo from a submarine one mile away under water, while radio waves, traveling at the speed of light, would echo from the ionosphere 50 miles away in one half of a thousandth of a second. Taylor, Young, and L. A. Gebhard of NRL, who built the radio pulse apparatus, followed up the proposal of Breit and Tuve in a co-operative effort and, together with Breit and Tuve, they made the first measurement of distance to a faraway reflecting object by timing the flight of pulses of electromagnetic energy. This was done in 1925 (Fig. 4). Their operation still was not what is known as radar, since the transmitter and receiver were separated by about eight miles and carefully isolated from each other. Furthermore, the pulses were much too long for location of ships or aircraft, the sensitivity would have been too low for radar if the pulses *could* have been sufficiently shortened, the ratio of time interval between pulses to pulse duration was much too low, and the radio frequencies were too low for practical use in radar. Besides, there seemed to be no need for attempting to convert it to radar, since detection of aircraft was not yet a military problem. In fact, flying aircraft inter-

* *Nature,* Vol. 116, 1925, p. 357.

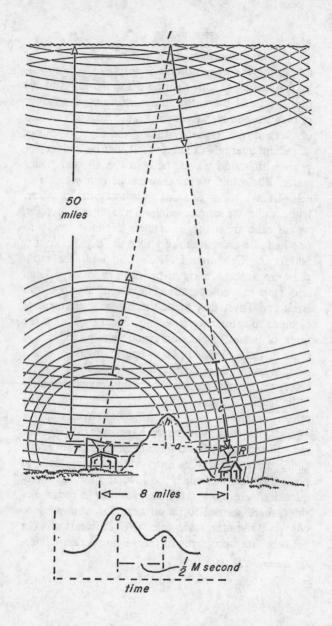

50 miles

8 miles

½ M second

time

fered with some of those early measurements of ionosphere height, but no one recognized the interference as being anything but a nuisance. The DTM-NRL ionosphere work of 1925 is important because it demonstrated the practicability of measuring large distances with radio pulses under certain limiting conditions.

A third link was forged in the idea chain when Hyland and Young discovered the detection of aircraft by radio in 1930. Unlike the earlier observation of the same phenomenon, their discovery was immediately followed up by two ideas. The first was that special radio apparatus be developed for the purpose of detecting aircraft. The second was that the pulse method be used. Both ideas were born of the mating of newly discovered knowledge to the problem of defense against the *potential* military threat of aircraft as machines of war. The two ideas again illustrate that a person making new discoveries must be intimately familiar with and interested in problems to be solved if he is to be effective in applying his discoveries to the solution of those problems.

Fig. 4. First use of radio pulses to measure height of ionosphere, in 1925. Transmitter, T, sends out pulse, a, which appears being reflected at b from ionosphere, I, 50 miles above the earth, to return to the earth at c. Receiver, R, spaced 8 miles from transmitter and partially shielded therefrom by hill, h, receives pulse, a, directly from transmitter, and later receives reflected portion of same pulse at c. Insert shows receiver output, which consists of a large direct signal, a, followed about one half millisecond later by a smaller reflected signal, c.

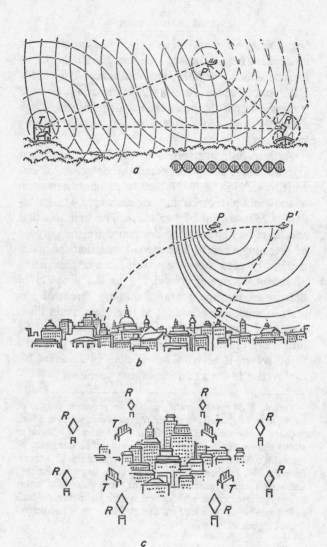

Developing Pulse Radar

The birth of the pulse radar idea in 1930 was a stillbirth. It was recognized that to be useful the apparatus must satisfy definite criteria: The transmitter and receiver would have to be close together, the pulses would have to be shorter than the ionosphere measuring pulses by a factor of 20 to 50 without shortening the time between pulses, the pulse power would have to be higher by a large factor, and all at a frequency 3 to 10 times higher. This combination of requirements seemed so far beyond the capabilities of existing technology that the idea was dropped without even a written record. After all, no one likes to be considered stupid, and this certainly looked like a stupid idea. However, the idea of developing radio apparatus for aircraft detecting was accepted, first by Dr. Taylor, then by the Bureau of Engineering, and work started immediately. The apparatus configuration (Fig. 5) with which the discovery was made

---

FIG. 5. (a) Second radar "discovery," 1930. Airplane, P, flying past receiver and transmitter, reflects some of transmitted energy into receiver. As airplane moves, the path length T to P to R changes, and so alternately cancels and reinforces the direct wave from T to R, giving rise to fluctuating signal in receiver as shown in insert.

(b) Problem: Sound travels so slowly that sound locator, S, gives warnings that are inaccurate and too late for defensive action.

(c) Idea: Use radio for detection of approaching aircraft, and protect cities with a ring of high frequency transmitters, T, and receivers, R.

was used to study the phenomenon and to determine its potential usefulness. With transmitter and receiver separation of 3 miles, and careful screening of the receiver from the transmitter by intervening hills and the "blind spot" in the receiving antenna, and with 500 watts of steady tone being radiated from the transmitter on a frequency of 29 megacycles, the apparatus could detect the presence of an airplane in flight at distances out to 40 miles. Neither the distance nor the direction to the airplane was determined by this method. The pilot of the airplane had to give the experimenters his location.

This work went on at NRL for three and a half years, from the fall of 1930 until March 1934. Its value obviously lay in the direction of air warning systems for large areas, such as cities and military bases, with a central transmitter surrounded by a network of receivers. Since the protection of such areas was solely an Army responsibility, the Secretary of the Navy, on January 9, 1932, transmitted to the Secretary of the Army a disclosure of the method, with the suggestion that the Army undertake further development for such purposes. Meanwhile, at NRL the growing sense of need for protection of ships from hostile aircraft accompanied the growing realization that the "beat" method was unsuitable for shipboard use. Transmitter and receiver would have to be on the same ship, rendering adequate isolation of the two virtually impossible, but even if that difficulty could be overcome, the method could then give neither range nor bearing to targets, nor could it tell whether a detected airplane was approaching or retreating. Then late in 1933 or early in 1934—the orig-

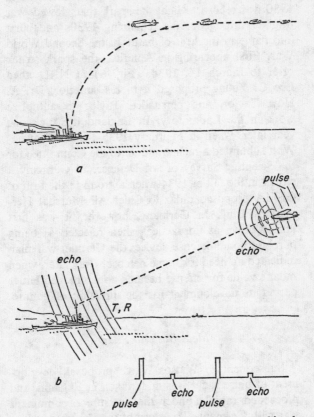

FIG. 6. (a) Problem: For aircraft warning on ships by radio, transmitter and receiver must be close together.

(b) Idea: Use short pulses with long spaces between, so transmitter will be "off the air" while the receiver is listening for echoes.

inal date was never recorded—the idea that died in 1930 was reborn to light the spark that glowed ever brighter throughout the remaining 1930s and burst into flame in the heat of battle in the Second World War. First appearing in America, the spark struck prior to March 14, 1934, (Fig. 6) at NRL when Leo C. Young proposed it to his superior, Dr. A. Hoyt Taylor, and persuaded Taylor to authorize work in the Laboratory. In England it struck one year later, when in February 1935 Robert Watson-Watt submitted a memorandum to the Committee for the Scientific Survey of Air Defense. In Germany it struck in the fall of 1934 when a group in the firm of GEMA proposed radar to Chief Air Marshal Hermann Göring. In Germany, however, it was first turned down as impractical, then rejected as being purely a home defense device; the German war plan indicated no need for home defense! Only later, when radar's value for offense became apparent, did Hitler permit its development for the direction of gunfire.

Ideas Basic to Radar

Subsequent to Watson-Watt's proposal, development of pulse radar was undertaken in England, and proceeded rapidly under the pressure of imminent war with Germany. The story of the British development has been eloquently told by several authors*

* Sir Robert Watson-Watt, *The Pulse of Radar*, Dial Press, Inc., New York, 1959. Louis N. Ridenour, *Radar System Engineering*, McGraw-Hill Publishing Co., New York, 1947.

Sir Winston Churchill and the English novelist C. P. Snow

and need not be repeated here. In America the development of pulse radar started on March 14, 1934, at the U. S. Naval Research Laboratory, and continued to and on through World War II, and after the war to some quite astounding postwar developments. But this constitutes the invention phase of radar, and before we get into that, we have a little more to say about the idea phase.

The ideas basic to radar are

1) that electromagnetic radiation at high radio frequency be employed for the detection and location of remote objects, or "targets,"

2) that the radiation be sent out in pulses not more than a very few microseconds in duration, separated by time intervals tens to thousands of times greater than the pulse duration,

3) that reflections or "echoes" of the short pulses scattered back from targets be received and displayed by a receiver in close proximity to the transmitter,

4) that distance to targets be determined by measuring the time of travel of pulses to the target and back, and

5) that direction to targets be determined by using highly directive antennas for transmitter, or for receiver, or for both.

All five ideas were essential to original radar. The earliest historical record of the combination of these five ideas is in my own official laboratory record, which chronicles the development from its start in the March 14, 1934, suggestion by Mr. Young. Why,

---

also have referred in their writings to the British work on radar.

then, have earlier discoveries and ideas in 1922, 1925, and 1930 been included in the discovery and idea phases of radar? And since these earlier events were included, why did I omit certain other events which have been mentioned by others as contributing to the development of radar? For example, it has been argued that since the reflection of radio waves by metallic objects was first demonstrated by Heinrich Hertz in 1887, the observations of Taylor, Young, and Hyland in 1922 and 1930 did not constitute discovery, and the credit therefore should go instead to Hertz. However, even after Hertz's discovery had been published and well known for over 50 years, no radar ever resulted, nor were the contributions of those who did originate the idea of radar guided or influenced by Hertz's discovery.

It has also been argued that in June 1922 Marconi suggested the use of beamed very high frequency radio waves to detect ships in darkness and fog, and that he thus deserved some credit for radar, or at least for the work of Taylor and Young in September 1922. But no work was done on the problem as a result of Marconi's speech,* and no radar resulted from his suggestions. Taylor and Young were not attempting to verify his suggestion, since they were not trying to get *reflections;* their discovery originated with signal cutoff, not signal reflection, and their proposed application did not involve reflection of radio energy. In 1923 a patent was issued to Mr. Herman Loewy, an Austrian, for a radio detection device in which the radio transmission would consist of a sig-

* "Radio Telegraphy," *Proc. IRE,* Vol. 10, No. 4, 1922, p. 237.

nal which was "chopped" so as to form short pulses with equally short spaces between pulses. At first this looks a little like radar, but the presence of more than one target would render it useless. Obviously, therefore, it was not radar and no radar system ever resulted from it.

On the other hand, Taylor and Young are the men who authorized, supervised, and supported the original development of radar, and the events of 1922, 1925, and 1930 were all a part of their experience contributing directly and leading up to the development.

It will be interesting to explore a little more into the reasons why the radar idea died in 1930, and was reborn in 1934 to live an abundant life. The explanation is to be found partly in the advancing "state of the art," and partly in the increasing urgency of finding a solution to the problem. We are concerned here with the state of the art, and particularly with electronic components which were essential to the development of radar but did not exist in 1930, or which existed but were inadequately developed. Consider first the cathode ray tube.

Technical Advances

Radar had to repeat in rapid succession (literally thousands of times a second) the precise measurement of a series of varying time intervals of only a few microseconds duration, and display the values of all those time intervals to the operator continuously. The only such device that performed satisfactorily was the cathode ray tube. In 1930 that tube was still under development, and not readily available, even for laboratory research purposes. In 1934 it was in wide use. Consider also the transmitting tube. Radar needed a transmitter that would generate hundreds or even thousands of watts of power in a pulse only a few microseconds long at a frequency of tens, if not hundreds, of megacycles. In 1930 there was no transmitting tube in existence that could approach this performance, even with high efficiency circuits, and the short pulse requirement meant broad band, low efficiency circuits. In 1934 a new line of transmitting tubes had appeared which were capable of operating under the extreme voltage conditions imposed by radar, and at the very high frequencies required by radar. And there was the receiver problem. Radar requires the same special types of receiving tubes and components as ultra high frequency television, but television even at ordinary high frequency had not yet been developed in 1930. By 1934 receiving tubes developed for television service could be obtained in limited quantities from tube development laboratories. These included the screened grid tube; the low capacitance, high mutual conductance output tube; and, above all, the famous ultra high frequency "acorn" tube. The ionosphere apparatus, with its low frequency, long pulses, low peak power, and isolated receiver needed none of these special components.

CHAPTER 3

ILLUMINATION OF THE TARGET

In order to comprehend the invention phase of any development we need to know what constitutes invention. Invention is a puzzle-solving game. If you like to solve puzzles, the chances are that you could become a good inventor, and that you would enjoy it. There are three essential stages to invention. First there must be a puzzle, or a problem to be solved, one that has never been solved before if it is to be a "first" invention. Second, there must be an idea that will solve the problem. The idea is the spark of life which, when applied to the problem, brings into being a new entity, a "something" that did not exist before. It is the origin of an invention, albeit one yet unborn, for the invention cannot be said to be really born until it has passed the third stage. This final stage is proof that it works, or, as it is called in patent law, "reduction to practice."

Perhaps it is now easy to see why invention is called a creative process. In one sense, any new creation, the generation and construction of something built on an idea or ideas that have never before been expressed in quite the same way, may be called invention. Thus an original form of poetry, sculpture, writing, painting, musical composition, or architecture may be called an invention just as much as a new type of engine, a new type of can opener, or a new type of pulse circuit for radar. Some would even go so far as to say that a new piece of original art in any field of artistic self-expression would be invention, even if only conventional art forms were employed.

All this background on the creative aspect of invention leads up to a very important point. The artist, the poet, the sculptor, author, composer, architect, all feel themselves closely identified with the things they personally have created. Their artistic fruits are peculiarly their own "personal property," and though as objects these fruits may be bought and sold in the market place, each creation remains a part of the person who created it. To ascribe to a rival, or to a stranger, or even to a non-competing friend, the results of one's own creative effort, is almost like taking away his own children. Should it seem strange then that an inventor, who is just as much a creative artist, should feel the same way about his own inventions? But when the same invention is made by several different inventors at different times, as usually does happen, a claim of priority established for one leaves little to be claimed by any other. So inventing can have its disappointments too, and in the inventions that produced radar the disappointments have been many. But just what were the inventions that produced radar? Actually there were many, over forty

High Radiofrequency for Detection
Microsecond Pulses Widely Spaced
Reception at Point of Transmission
Distance by Time of Flight of Pulses
Direction by Directive Antennas

1

RADAR IDEA

Radio Pulse Generators
Range Calibrators
Duplexers
Precision Angle Circuits
Precision Ranging Circuits
Multiple Tube Oscillators
Automatic Tracking Circuits
Many Others

3

RADAR INVENTIONS to implement RADAR IDEA

Illumination of Targets
Reception of Echoes
Transmitter-Receiver Closeness
Target Position Indication
Precision Tracking

2

RADAR PROBLEMS solved by RADAR INVENTIONS

FIG. 7. Relationship between Radar Idea, Radar Problems that had to be solved, and Radar Inventions which solved the problems.

in fact, for which this author has received patents. Rather than try to describe these separately, we will look at the basic problems (Fig. 7) that had to be solved, and the ideas that solved them.

Radio Waves

Let us consider first the problem of illuminating the target. For the target we select a small airplane not more than ten miles away. Have you ever seen a four-passenger airplane at a distance of ten miles? I have. The air was phenomenally clear and visibility was the best that I have ever seen. The airplane was just the tiniest speck that I could barely make out though I knew exactly where to look and shaded my eyes carefully with both hands. That airplane was illuminated by bright sunlight, and the surfaces I could see were probably receiving about two kilowatts of radiant energy from the sun. To get an equivalent amount of radiofrequency energy on the plane ten miles away from me, I would have to have a radio transmitter that could generate many kilowatts. Let us see now just how this can be done.

Radio waves, like light from the sun, are electromagnetic radiation. But whereas light from the sun is on wavelengths of a small fraction of a millionth of a centimeter, the radio wavelengths used in the first radar experiments were several meters. Light is most easily generated by heating material until it glows. The surface temperature of the sun is about 6000°K, but a tungsten wire heated to 2000°K will also give a bright light. That is how an ordinary electric light bulb is made to give light. At radio wavelengths, however, it is easier to radiate energy by causing radiofrequency current to flow in a conductor. The current in the conductor may be thought of as electrons traveling, or "flowing," along the conductor at very nearly the speed of light. When electrons flowing in a conducting wire come to the end of the wire, they are reflected back along the wire just as a rubber ball is bounced back from a wall. If electrons are made to start flowing in one direction along a short piece of wire, they will bounce back and forth be-

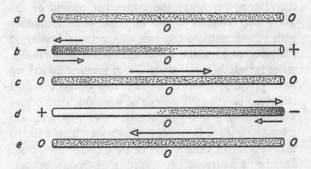

Fig. 8. Position and motions of electrons in a half-wave resonator.

(a) No signal present. Electrons uniformly spaced throughout wire, all in random motion, with no net flow.

(b) Signal present. Electrons bouncing off left end of wire, making that end negative. Few electrons at right end, making that end positive.

(c) Electrons, having bounced off left end of wire, are flowing toward right end.

(d) Electrons bouncing off right end of wire, making that end negative, and the left end positive.

(e) Electrons having bounced off right end are flowing back toward left end.

tween the two ends of the wire, flowing first in one direction and then the other. This constitutes an alternating current in the wire. The repeated back and forth flow is called oscillation. One complete round trip of the electrons, including two bounces, one from each end of the wire, is called one cycle of the oscillation. The number of cycles in one second is the frequency of the alternating current. Since we may think of the electrons as moving with constant speed, the frequency will depend on the length of the wire. The longer the wire, the longer the time required for the round trip, the fewer the cycles per second or the lower the frequency. We may associate frequency with wavelength. In the case of electrons flowing in the piece of wire, the wavelength is the effective distance traveled in one cycle. From the description we have given, it is apparent that this distance is just twice the length of the piece of wire. Such a piece of wire is called a half-wave resonator (Fig. 8), since it resonates with a frequency whose wavelength in the wire is just twice the length of the piece of wire. Such alternating currents are called radiofrequency currents when their frequency is between 10 kcs and 30,000 kcs.

The Radar Beam

Now a curious thing about an electron is that when it bounces, or accelerates, it sends energy out into space just as a floating cork moving up and down on water sends waves out on the surface of the water. This energy is half electric and half magnetic in na-

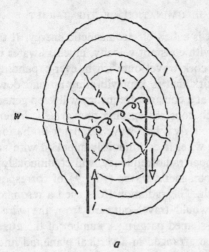

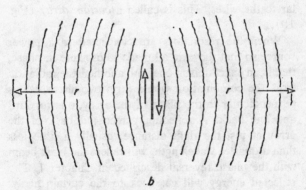

FIG. 9. Three kinds of electromagnetic radiation.

(a) An electric current, *i*, flowing through a resistance wire, *w*, generates heat which is projected as radiant heat waves, *h*, and light, which is projected as light waves, *l*.

(b) A half-wave resonator in which radiofrequency current flows at resonant frequency, projects radio waves, *r*.

ture, so it is called electromagnetic energy. It travels in space with constant velocity, much as water waves from the cork travel outward in ever-expanding circles. A cork that is kept vibrating up and down on the water at a constant frequency will keep generating waves with constant spacing or *wavelength* between crests. Similarly a half-wave resonator in the form of a straight wire, if continuously supplied with energy at the proper radiofrequency, will continuously radiate electromagnetic waves (Fig. 9) of corresponding wavelength. The radiation from such a resonator, or antenna, would travel outward from the wire in a doughnut-shaped pattern. A number of these resonators can be arranged in a vertical plane, all lined up in the same direction, spaced a half wavelength on centers in directions both parallel to and perpendicular to the wires. This is called a *curtain array* (Fig. 10).

When the resonators are connected to a power source so that they are all made to oscillate in phase, that is, in exact unison one with another, the radiation from the combination would form two sharp beams perpendicular to the plane of the array, one forward and one back. A reflecting screen put back of the array at just the right distance, usually a little less than a quarter wavelength, will reflect the back beam with the phase reversal described in Chapter 1. The reflected energy will get back to the curtain array, just in time to add to the forward beam, resulting in a single beam with all the radiated energy in that beam. This radiation corresponds to the *radar beam* that illuminates targets with radiofrequency electromagnetic radiation. There are many other ways of

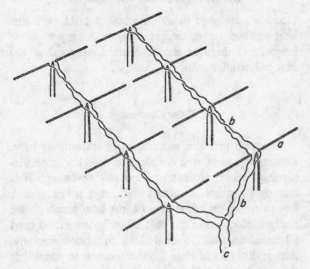

Fig. 10. A radio curtain array with 16 half-wave resonators, *a*, interconnected with feed lines, *b*, and connected to radiofrequency terminal equipment, *c*.

forming a radio beam. The best way depends on what frequency is used, and how sharp a beam is desired. But the first radar beams were formed in the manner described. This was existing art, which means it was already in use, and new beam antennas therefore did not have to be developed for radar.

Our first radar problem was to generate the radiofrequency energy. The first question to answer was, "What frequency should be used?" The wavelength should be no greater than twice the smallest target anticipated if good reflection was to be assured. This placed a long wavelength limit at 20 to 30 meters, corresponding to a frequency of 15 to 10 megacycles.

Good results were being obtained at NRL with the beat method on 60 megacycles, or 5 meters wavelength, and this was chosen as the frequency for the first pulse radar work.

Pulse Operation

The next problem was choice of transmitter tube. Remember, now, that we want to detect a small airplane at 10 miles distance, and to give enough illumination for that is going to require a lot of power. Let us try to get some idea of just how much power really is required in the pulse. The beat method used a transmitter that illuminated the target continuously, thus giving lots of time for the receiver to "look" at the target. It was like taking a photograph on a dark cloudy day and using a long time exposure to get a picture on the film. But in the pulse method the receiver can see the target only for the very short flash of the pulse; the power level during the pulse must be many times greater than the power level for the beat method. This method is like taking a photograph with a very short time exposure, which requires very bright light to get a picture. A fast camera may have a shutter speed setting as short as one one-thousandth of a second. But the pulse length (shutter speed) of this first radar was one one-hundred-thousandth of a second, or just one hundred times as fast.

Now one one-hundred-thousandth of a second is ten microseconds, and there was a good reason for picking that length of time for the pulse. Electromagnetic energy, such as light and radio waves, travels in space at a speed of about 186,000 miles a second, or about two tenths of a mile in one microsecond. In ten microseconds then it will travel about two miles. But in radar it has to travel out to the target, then back to the receiver, so in ten microseconds it will travel to a target and back when the target is one mile away. In pulse radar, transmitter and receiver would be arranged close together, and it would not be possible for the receiver to detect target echoes while the transmitter was on. With a ten microsecond pulse therefore, the receiver would be blind to all targets closer than one mile. Also, if two or more airplanes were separated by less than one mile, their echoes would overlap, and one could not tell how many planes were there. Obviously, it would be better for radar if the pulse could be much shorter, but then the difficulties become greater also. Ten microseconds was chosen because it was not so difficult that we could not generate it, and yet it was short enough to keep from "blinding" the receiver to targets more than one mile away.

We have implied that the relationship between pulse length and power level during the pulse in pulse radar is the same as the relationship between shutter speed and light intensity in taking pictures, assuming a constant lens speed or aperture. Except for the help one can get in radar from seeing the same echo repeated over and over, the relationships are similar. A given film exposure results from a given total quantity of light energy on the film, whether it is little light for a long time, or much light for a short time. The total quantity of energy is the *intensity* or *power level* times the length of exposure time. Likewise in

51

radar, the illumination from one pulse is proportional to the total energy radiated in one pulse, and that total is the power level during the pulse times the pulse length.

Now another quantity had to be known, and that was how much time to allow between pulses. We have seen already that the time of travel of radio waves from the radar to the target and back is about ten microseconds for each mile to the target. We have chosen ten miles for target distance. That fixes 100 microseconds as the shortest time interval between the beginning of pulses. So we made the pulses come every 100 microseconds, and since the pulses were 10 microseconds long, 90 microseconds elapsed between pulses. If echoes were received, the receiver could see targets between one and ten miles away.

We now have accumulated enough facts to start putting them together and begin to reach for some conclusions. Our pulse is 10 microseconds long, and we have one pulse every 100 microseconds, so there will be ten thousand pulses a second, and the transmitter will actually be radiating power one tenth of the time. In the beat method the transmitter is radiating power all the time. We have said that the ability to see a target depends on the total energy with which the target is illuminated "while we are looking." With the beat method we can look at one target for much longer than one ten-thousandth of a second, but with pulse radar we can look at many pulses from the same target. Actually, for any one target and by either method of "looking" we have the same total time to look. This equality of time interval suggests the possibility that the same "average" power would be required in each case, and the condition would be true if both systems were designed to the theoretical limit of sensitivity. Usually, however, some loss of sensitivity does occur in going from continuous operation to pulse operation, and we may conclude that average power for pulse radar must be as great as or greater than average power for the beat method. Therefore, with the pulse transmitter on only one tenth of the time, the power level during the pulse would have to be at least ten times as great as the power level required for the beat method (Fig. 11). But the beat method already was using all the power that could be generated in those days. The problem would have been hopeless had it not been for some new tricks made possible by short pulses. To understand these we must take a closer look at how a vacuum tube works.

The Vacuum Tube

We will describe a simple triode as a vacuum tube with three electrodes inside an evacuated glass envelope. Right in the center will be one electrode, the *cathode*. It is a specially treated tungsten wire and is frequently referred to as the filament. This filament resembles the filament in an electric lamp, and, like the lamp filament, it becomes white-hot when electric current flows in the wire. When hot, it gives off not only light but also electrons, and special treatments sometimes increase vastly the rate at which it will supply electrons. Surrounding the cathode and well spaced from it is the anode, or *plate*. The plate

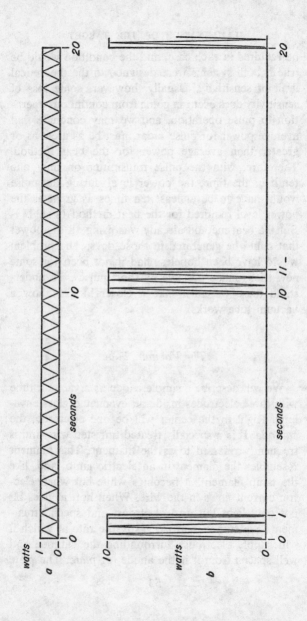

is usually in the form of a hollow cylinder, and it *collects* the electrons that are supplied by the cathode. When a source of electric power, such as a battery, is applied to these two electrodes, with the negative battery terminal connected to the cathode and the positive terminal to the anode, the electrons supplied by the cathode will be drawn to the anode and flow into the battery. Between the cathode and the anode, and usually quite close to the cathode, is a wire screen or cage that completely surrounds and encloses the cathode. This third electrode is called the *grid*. Electrons that flow from the cathode to the anode must pass through the holes in the grid.

Electrons are most unsociable creatures. They act as if they were all afraid of each other, always running away and staying just as far apart from each other as they can. Solid materials act as prisons that keep them confined in the material. In conductors the electrons are free to roam through the material, and they tend to crowd to the outer surface in such a way as to keep as far away as possible from one another. It is as if they could smell each other and did not like the smell. The influence which they seem to smell is an electric field. The electric field emanates from an electric charge carried by each electron. Engineering convention has called the electric charge

---

FIG. 11. Pulse and continuous wave (cw) equivalent energy. Energy equals Power times Time.

(a) CW power of one watt for 20 seconds is 20 joules of energy, averaging one joule per second.

(b) Pulse power of 10 watts for one second, repeated at ten second intervals, is 10 joules every 10 seconds, averaging one joule per second.

on an electron a negative charge. A conductor that contains a high concentration of free electrons is said to have a negative potential. Two separate conductors having different concentrations of free electrons in them have different potentials, and we say that a potential difference or a voltage exists between them. The conductors are then called negative or positive relative to each other. When two conductors at different potentials are connected together, electrons rush from the negative to the positive conductor until both conductors reach the same potential. A battery is a chemical pump that pumps electrons from the positive terminal to the negative terminal; the negative terminal is crowded with electrons trying to get out, while the positive terminal is always hungry for electrons. When a "bunch" of electrons bounce back and forth between the ends of a half-wave resonator, the charge they carry with them makes first one end of the resonator negative, then the other end. The potential at each end of the resonator then oscillates at the frequency of the radiofrequency current in the resonator. This oscillating potential is called a radiofrequency voltage.

In a vacuum tube, as in most electrical circuits, absolute potential has no significance. Everything depends on potential differences. The electrons are easily captured by the anode because the anode is kept positive relative to the cathode and grid. If the grid were positive relative to the cathode, then electrons would be captured by the grid also. When the grid is the same potential as the cathode, the electrons from the cathode can't even smell it, and they flow freely through the holes in the grid to be captured by the anode. When the grid is made a little negative relative to the cathode, it begins to smell bad to the electrons from the cathode, and those that are not going too fast will turn back instead of going through the holes. Electrons that are going too fast to stop will sneak through the holes without touching the grid, and be captured by the anode. The more negative the grid relative to the cathode, the fewer the electrons that get through the holes. The grid voltage that just turns back all electrons is called the cutoff voltage. The grid voltage relative to the cathode is called *grid bias*. Since the grid itself collects very few electrons, it does not require much power to change its voltage. Thus the grid acts as an adjustable gate that controls the rate of flow of electrons from the cathode to the anode. And since the electron flow from cathode to anode is in the main power circuit of the vacuum tube, the grid is a true valve (Fig. 12) that turns the main power off and on without itself absorbing much power.

The power limitation on transmitting vacuum tubes in 1934 was determined by the temperature of the tube elements, particularly the anode, where most of the power loss in the tube is absorbed. The higher the power level, the hotter the anode, and if the anode gets too hot, it will melt or "boil off some gas" and so spoil the tube. But temperature is determined by average power. When the tube is made to generate very short pulses spaced far apart, then the power level during the pulse can be increased without overheating the tube. In fact, if temperature were the only limitation and efficiency remained constant, it would be simple just to increase the anode voltage until the

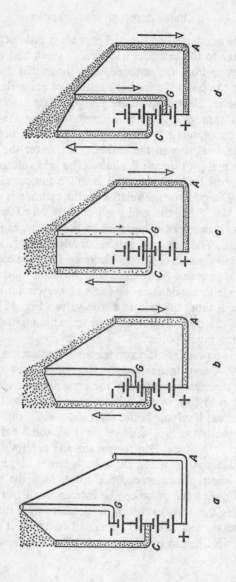

a   b   c   d

tube gave ten times the power during the pulse. Then, being on only one tenth the time, the temperature of the anode should be the same as under normal operating conditions. However, increasing anode voltage causes more electrons to flow from cathode to anode, and at normal operating temperature the cathode cannot supply electrons fast enough to run the tube at ten times the normal power level. The second limitation is therefore the rate at which the cathode can supply electrons to the anode, or cathode *emission* as it is called.

There was a very simple solution to the cathode emission limit. A small increase in cathode heating current produces a large increase in cathode emission. Increasing the heating current only 10 per cent gave nearly double the cathode emission, and still allowed reasonable operating life for the tube. This greater cathode emission permitted further increase in pulse power until another limiting influence was found. Higher power brings higher radiofrequency voltage at the tube terminals, and when tubes were operated on

---

FIG. 12. A vacuum tube is a valve that controls the flow of electrons. In these diagrams cathode, *C*, grid, *G*, and anode, *A*, are shown as vertical "pipes" held in position by a battery. Electrons are pushed to the top by the hot cathode, then flow down hill and through the "pipes" to the battery as permitted by the grid position, or potential.

(a) Cutoff grid bias
(b) Slightly negative grid bias
(c) Zero grid bias
(d) Slightly positive grid bias

Note that the current flowing through the cathode is equal to the sum of the currents in anode and grid, as indicated by the length of the vertically drawn arrows.

pulses of power many times their intended operating power level, the high radiofrequency voltages would ionize the air around the tube terminals and actually spark across the terminals. The only cure was to use tubes with large spacings between terminals and to shield the terminals with round metal knobs to eliminate sharp points or edges where the sparks could start.

With all these precautions taken, it was possible to operate transmitter tubes at pulse power levels ten to twenty times their average power ratings. These operating conditions paid huge dividends in another manner. You will recall that radar required not only very high power pulses, but this high power at very high radiofrequencies. Increasing the operating voltages also increased the frequency at which the transmitter could be made to operate. To understand this we need to see how a vacuum tube can be made to generate radiofrequency oscillations.

We have seen how electrons in a vacuum tube flow from the cathode, through the grid, to the anode. The grid acts as a valve controlling the number of electrons that get through to the anode, and the controlling factor is the voltage on the grid relative to the cathode. We could turn the electron flow in the tube on and off by just switching the grid terminal on the tube back and forth between zero bias and a high negative bias. At zero bias many electrons reach the anode, while at the negative bias no electrons reach the anode. If some of the electrons on the anode were allowed to return directly to the grid through an external connection, their negative charges would tend to make the grid negative at the very time we were trying to make it zero, so this would not work. But if the external connection were a long piece of wire, it would take some time for the electrons to get back to the grid to cut off the current in the tube.

This delayed action allows the anode to feed a lot of electrons into the wire before they reach the grid and cut off the current. When these electrons reach the grid, they cannot go any farther, and they bounce back to the anode through the same wire. When they have all bounced away from the grid, the grid returns to zero bias and allows electrons to flow again from cathode to anode in the tube. These electrons reach the anode at the same time as the first electrons bouncing back from the grid in the external wire. The cycle then starts over as the growing cloud of electrons bounces back to the grid to cut off the tube current again.

Now we have a bunch of electrons bouncing back and forth between the two ends of a piece of wire, and in so doing they turn the electron current off and on in a vacuum tube while the resulting intermittent current in the vacuum tube keeps adding to the bunch of bouncing electrons in the wire. The repeating cycle is called oscillation, and the circuit combination is called an oscillator circuit (Fig. 13). The energy source is the battery that keeps the anode positive relative to the cathode by supplying electrons to the cathode.

It is now apparent that the external feedback circuit is a half-wave resonator, and the delayed-action feedback time corresponds to half a cycle of the resonant frequency of the feedback resonator as described on page 46. This is an important concept

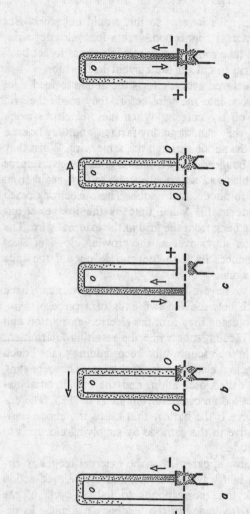

which we will use when we consider the stability of a radar receiver. But first, what has it to do with effects of high voltage on transmitter frequency?

We have assumed that all the delay in feedback was provided by the external circuit. However, it does take some time for the electrons in the tube to go from grid to anode. Electrons in a vacuum seem to move much more slowly than they do in a metallic conductor; the delay inside the tube has to be considered, too. To generate higher frequency oscillations, the external circuit delay is made shorter. When it is made nearly as short as the delay inside the tube, the electrons in the tube reach the anode too late to add to the bunch of electrons in the external circuit, and oscillation cannot be maintained. Increasing anode voltage makes the electrons in the tube move faster, thus reducing the delay inside the tube, and enabling the tube to generate oscillations at higher frequencies.

FIG. 13. How oscillation is generated. A folded half-wave resonator, *o*, is connected to grid and anode of a vacuum tube. + and − signs indicate only the potential differences due to electrons oscillating in the resonator.

(a) Electrons flowing to anode in the vacuum tube pass into resonant circuit.

(b) Electrons in resonant circuit flow toward grid and start cutting off electron flow in tube.

(c) Electrons in resonant circuit have reached grid, cut off electron flow in the tube, and started bouncing back to the anode.

(d) Electrons in resonant circuit bouncing back toward anode, allow grid to start passing more electrons in the tube.

(e) Electrons in resonant circuit and electrons in tube all reach anode at the same time, and cycle starts over again.

In 1934 there was no really high-power transmitting tube at 60 mc, and such tubes as were available were quite inefficient at that frequency. The increase in anode voltage made possible by the pulse technique was, therefore, a great help in getting the desired high power at high frequency.

The Multivibrator

A tube type to satisfy these considerations was selected and a transmitter built with two tubes in a *push-pull* oscillator circuit—that is, a circuit in which one tube drives each end of the half-wave resonator. The problem of keying this transmitter with a 10 microsecond pulse ten thousand times a second was easily solved with a *multivibrator*, which is described in Chapter 5.

Having built a radio transmitter for illuminating targets with short pulses of radiofrequency energy, we desired to find out whether echoes from aircraft could be detected with those short pulses. For eight months we had dreamed and thought and planned and worked on a fantastic idea, knowing it could be doomed, but fired with a burning hope that it was destined to succeed. Many problems remained to be solved in receiving and indicating echoes from targets, if there were any echoes to receive. It was very important to find out as early as possible whether there was any need even to try to solve these other problems. All we needed was to determine whether pulse echoes would occur in sufficient energy to be detected at all. So a test was set up in which a laboratory model of a very high gain, high frequency experimental receiver with a cathode ray indicator and a separate receiving antenna was used to test for the presence of radar echoes. The pulse transmitter and keyer were in one building with a directive antenna on the roof. The receiver and indicator were in an adjacent building with a similar directive antenna on its roof. The keyer in one building and the indicator in the other were connected by a cable for synchronizing the indication with the transmitter pulses. The two antennas were pointed out across the Potomac River, which flowed past the Laboratory, and a small airplane was flown up and down the river through the radar beam at low altitude.

Echo signals from this airplane were observed while the transmitter was off in the intervals between

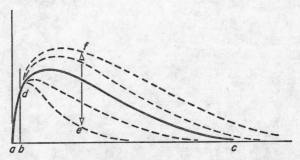

FIG. 14. First signals demonstrating reception of echoes from aircraft during intervals between short transmitted pulses, December 1934. Transmitted pulse of ten microseconds occurs from *a* to *b*. Receiver "ringing" from transmitted signal appears as solid line from *d* to *c*. When airplane flew across the beam, receiver output fluctuated between *e* and *f* as shown by dotted lines.

pulses. This was proof that short pulse echo energy was sufficient to justify going ahead with solution of the receiver and indicator problems. Thus (Fig. 14) did pulse radar pass its first test with an airplane target in December 1934.

CHAPTER 4

RECEPTION OF RADAR ECHOES

The most difficult problems in the development of radar were in the receiver. Radar imposed four severe and unusual demands on this component. A complete description of these demands, and of how they were met, involves much radio technology. In this chapter we present the basic ideas involved. The more technical details will follow in Chapter 5.

At some time everyone has played with a swing of some sort. If you stand in an ordinary swing and "pump" by moving your body to and fro in just the right manner, you can gradually build up a very high swinging motion. Each pumping effort adds only a little to the height of the swinging motion, and a very high swinging motion requires many "pumps," each done at just the right time in the "swing." When you have achieved a high swinging motion, you can stand still in the swing and "coast," and you will keep on swinging for a long, long time before the swing comes completely to rest.

Now the swing with you in it is a pendulum. Its

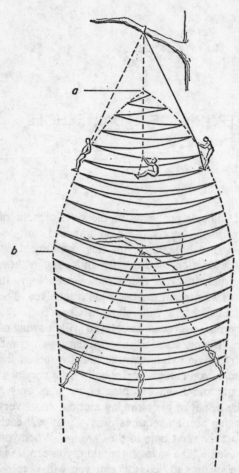

FIG. 15. Slow build-up and decay of swinging motion illustrates a high Q resonant circuit. Pumping motion builds up amplitude gradually from a to b. After b, coasting without pumping continues for a very long time.

swinging motion is called oscillation. One complete "round trip" forth and back again is one cycle of the oscillation. The time for one cycle is called the period of the oscillation, and depends only on the length of the swing rope. This is similar to the half-wave resonator for electrons, where the period of the oscillation depends only on the length of the wire in which the electrons bounce back and forth between the ends. Both the swing and the electron resonator are resonant systems. In both cases, the frequency corresponding to the time for one cycle is called the resonant or natural frequency.

Amplification

Because the swing will coast, or keep on oscillating by itself, for a long time, it is said to have a very low decrement, or low decrease or *decay* rate, or long decay time. Oscillatory or resonant circuits with this property are said to have a high *Q*, and are called *high Q circuits* (Fig. 15). Now suppose you were to grasp the bumper of an automobile and pull and push to make the car bounce up and down on its springs. The bouncing car also is an oscillatory circuit, but you will find that after the first couple of pushes you will not be able to make the car bounce any higher unless you exert much more force on the bumper. When you stop pulling and pushing, the car will stop bouncing almost at once. This particular circuit has a very high decrement, or high decay rate, or short decay time, and is said to have a low *Q* (Fig. 16).

When a radiofrequency signal is applied to a resonant radio circuit, the response in that circuit will build up gradually, as in the swing we just talked about. The length of time required for the circuit current to build up to full value, or to die away to a very low value, is proportional to the Q of the circuit. Another way to think of it is to consider that Q refers to the total "quantity" of electron energy that can be stimulated in the resonant circuit with a given signal. The greater the Q, the longer it takes any given signal to supply all the energy the circuit will take up, or *store*. When the signal applied is a short pulse, such as is used in radar, the Q must be low enough so that the circuit current will reach nearly full value in the very short time available during the pulse, and then will die away just as quickly when the pulse is over, in order to be ready for the next pulse. But if the Q is made lower than necessary to meet this condition, then the circuit response will be less, and amplification will be lost and noise increased. A radar receiver

FIG. 16. Fast build-up and decay of bouncing of car illustrates a low Q resonant circuit. Pulling and pushing builds up to full amplitude in about one cycle, from *a* to *b*. Amplitude decays to zero in about one cycle, at *c* to *d*, when pulling and pushing is discontinued.

has many resonant circuits, in a long chain, with each circuit driven by the voltage from the preceding circuit in the chain. Each circuit adds its own delay to the build-up and decay times of the receiver output, which operates some indicating device.

The first problem was to find the Q value for each circuit in the chain that would just permit the receiver output to rise to nearly full value during the pulse. The mathematical complexity of calculating the combined effect of all the circuits was a stumbling block until a published article on the subject was found in a French scientific magazine.* With the help of this

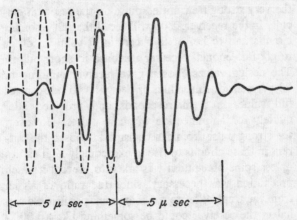

FIG. 17. A constant amplitude radiofrequency pulse 5 microseconds long (dotted line), when applied at the input of a 5-microsecond time constant receiver, builds up and decays at the output as shown by the solid line.

* René Mesny, "Time Constants, Build-up Time and Decrements," *l'Onde Electrique*, Vol. 13, June 1934, pp. 237–243.

article the experimenters derived the relationship between circuit Q, pulse length, and receiver gain for any number of resonant circuits. This calculation was accomplished early in 1935, about the time the famous *acorn*-type high frequency receiving tube became available. It was found that with this type of tube the weakest echoes that could be received were amplified sufficiently (Fig. 17) to give a good target indication even with pulses as short as five microseconds! Thus was solved the problem of amplifying very weak pulses of very short duration without appreciably changing the pulse length.

The second problem had to do with the effects of the very strong transmitted pulse on the resonant circuits in the receiver. You will recall that all resonant circuits had to be set to a certain Q value in order to get fast enough receiver response to short pulses. The design values chosen gave receiver build-up to 90 per cent of full value, or decay to 10 per cent of full value, in 5 microseconds and provided adequately for amplification of short pulses. However, the strong pulse from the transmitter caused the current in these circuits to rise to exceedingly high values unless some precaution was taken to prevent it. Such precaution was necessary, since the ratio of signal from the transmitter to the maximum permissible signal in the receiver could be something like 10,000,-000,000,000,000, or ten thousand million million.

A receiver that would accomplish a decay of signal to $\frac{1}{10}$ value in 5 microseconds would require about 40 microseconds to recover from this transmitter signal, and would continue to "ring" or oscillate for another 10 microseconds, thus blanking out the first

5 miles after the transmitter pulse. The cure (Fig. 18) was to prevent the resonant circuits from building up such high oscillating current when driven so hard by the transmitted pulse. The high current limit in the receiver circuits is controlled in part by the grid bias on the receiver tubes. When this bias was zero on all but the last tubes in the receiving amplifier, the total circuit ring time from the transmitted pulse to the reception of echoes was made less than 5 microseconds.

The third problem concerned an effect analogous to eye accommodation in vision. When your eyes have become accustomed to seeing well in semidarkness, a sudden bright light will blind you for a few seconds. If the light has been on for even a moment, you can see nothing for some time when you turn it off again. Very gradually, however, your ability to see will come back. A radio receiver acts just the same way. When used right beside a transmitter, as it would be in radar, the receiver would be completely blinded, or *saturated,* by the strong signal from the transmitted pulse. Now if that were all that happened, it would not matter, for the receiver does not need to receive echoes while the transmitter is sending the pulse. That is one of the big advantages of the pulse method. But a conventional type of radio receiver would remain completely blind long after the pulse was sent, and possibly even for several seconds. Since all the echoes from airplanes come back in less than a thousandth of a second, none could be seen by the receiver.

The solution for this problem involves many technical details, which may be found in Chapter 5.

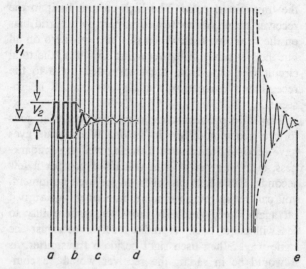

FIG. 18. Effect of amplitude limiting on receiver recovery time. The transmitted pulse occurs from a to b. V_1 represents transmitted signal amplitude in the receiver with no limiting. The signal peaks extend far beyond the limits of the page, and receiver ringing extends from b to e, blocking out all echoes that might occur in the interval b to e. V_2 represents the amplitude to which signal in the receiver is limited with zero bias on the grids and low voltage on the anodes. Receiver ringing is limited to the interval from b to c. The echo signal shown between c and d could not be received without limiting.

Suffice it to say here that the receiver was finally made to accommodate itself to violent changes in signal level so rapidly that within 5 microseconds after exposure to the full transmitted signal, it was ready to receive echo signals almost as if it hadn't even seen the transmitter!

Gain and Stability

Finally, there were unusual problems of gain and stability that had to be solved for the receiver. The over-all voltage gain of the average high-gain receiver of those days was usually about one million. The radar receiver had to give an unusually high output voltage in order to operate a cathode ray tube indicator, however, and that even with a very low input signal. Operation of the indicator required over-all voltage gain of nearly one hundred million. Of itself, this gain would not have been so great a problem if it were not for the fast response requirements we have been discussing. To understand this problem we must take another look at some of the things we discussed in Chapter 3.

There we saw that if some of the output voltage from a vacuum tube were delayed by a certain amount and then fed back to the grid, the tube would generate an alternating current signal, and we would say it was oscillating. The frequency of oscillation would be determined in part by the total delay from the grid, through the tube and circuit back to the grid. The gain in the tube required to produce oscillation need be only great enough to overcome losses in the circuit, due mainly to circuit resistance and losses by radiation of some of the energy into space. Ordinarily the required gain is quite low if all the output energy is fed back to the grid. The gain of one tube is usually enough for oscillation to occur with only a small part of the energy fed back. In a receiver where high gain is achieved with the use of several tubes, oscillation will be caused by an exceedingly small amount of feedback. Since oscillation of the receiver would interfere with its operation as an amplifier, it becomes necessary to go to a lot of trouble with shielding and filtering in order to get very high isolation between input and output to prevent oscillation of the receiver. With the higher gain required in the radar receiver this was even a more difficult problem. However, just preventing oscillation was far from the whole story.

Remember how the swing with you in it became a pendulum? Have you noticed that the frequency with which such a pendulum swings to and fro is constant? You can make it swing high, or you can make it swing just a little bit, but the frequency is always the same, and no matter how you push it, you cannot change the frequency at which it wants to go. This strong tendency to oscillate at only one fixed frequency is characteristic of all high Q circuits. From this property high Q circuits are sometimes called narrow band circuits because they will sustain oscillations over a very narrow band of frequencies only. Now remember the automobile bouncing up and down on its springs. This resonant circuit doesn't seem to care what frequency you produce when you push it. It will follow your pushing and pulling just about the same whether you go fast or slow—within reasonable limits, of course. This ability to follow any frequency over a considerable range of frequencies is characteristic of all low Q circuits. From this property low Q circuits are sometimes called broad band circuits because they will sustain oscillations over a relatively broad band of frequencies. At the beginning of this chapter we saw that the speed of response of a circuit to a change in input signal is determined by the Q of the circuit. So it follows that circuit bandwidth and speed of circuit response always go together. A narrow bandwidth circuit responds slowly, therefore is not suitable for amplifying short pulses, while a wide bandwidth circuit responds quickly and therefore is suitable for amplifying short pulses.

Now consider a radar receiver amplifier. It will have a high gain. Since it will have a fast response for amplifying short pulses, it will also be a broad band amplifier. It will have several amplifier tubes and resonant circuits all tuned to the same frequency. If such an amplifier had a minute amount of its output fed back to its input, it would oscillate. But now this oscillation would be on just one frequency. This frequency would be determined in part by the total signal delay from the input grid, and back through the amplifier and feedback path to the input grid. This is known as the total loop delay. Suppose that we can reduce the amount of feedback until the circuit just stops oscillating. This does not mean that there is no feedback. It means only that the feedback is not great enough to cancel all circuit losses. It may cancel nearly all these losses, however, at the one frequency determined by the loop delay. With circuit losses partially canceled at one frequency, the amplifier gain will be much higher at this frequency than at any other frequency. The circuit therefore becomes narrow band instead of wide band and loses its fast response. In order to regain fast response, the feedback must be reduced further until it actually does become zero for all practical purposes. This is a far more rigid requirement than that imposed by any other radio receivers of that day, and it was achieved by engineering design that exploited every precaution to eliminate feedback. Amplifier stages were shielded individually, all supply leads were individually filtered to each stage, tube mountings were handmade to provide the shortest possible radiofrequency return path for each stage, and all ground leads were brought to a common point on the chassis for grounding. In addition, frequency was changed several times in the receiver so that only moderate gain was required on any one frequency. When all these precautions were taken, the stray feedback was so low that no difference in bandwidth or response time could be detected when the gain was changed from its lowest value, for strong input signals, to full gain, where residual input noise gave full receiver output.

Thus we have identified four critical factors in which the radar receiver had to be very different from any other radio receiver of the time. (1) Amplification of very short pulses required tuned circuit Q values critically adjusted to the correct values, which were much lower than customary; (2) accommodation to vastly different signal levels had to be almost instantaneous; (3) reduction of transmitter-induced ringing of the receiver tuned circuits required the

78

lowest possible saturation level of the early stages of the receiver, achieved by zero grid bias and correspondingly low anode voltage; and (4) extreme precautions were necessary to achieve the required extraordinarily high gain with no feedback to "spoil" the short time constants so carefully designed into the receiver.

On the basis of the foregoing analysis calculations were carried out, design charts were drawn, and a complete receiver was designed and constructed in the spring and summer of 1935. When the receiver was completed, it was carefully adjusted to the proper Q values and resonant frequencies for all circuits, and tested. It performed in all respects just as predicted. However, after standing a few weeks while work progressed on other parts of the system, the receiver was tested again and found to have very low gain and response time much too short. Investigation disclosed that a slight amount of moisture absorbed by the coil forms lowered the Q of all circuits enough to throw it out of adjustment. Since all capacitances had been kept to the lowest possible value, maximum values had been obtained for the inductances, permitting maximum gain for a given Q. The resulting large change in receiver gain and response time caused by a small change in coil losses was a new experience in radio receivers. Although the material used in the coil forms conformed to standard practice at the time, it was necessary to throw away all the coils and make new ones with special new low-loss materials just then becoming available. This substitution cured the final receiver problem, and our radar receiver was ready to go to work. But now there were other things to consider.

Increasing the Effective Range

The test conducted in December 1934 had shown that sufficient pulse echo energy could be obtained on 60 megacycles to detect aircraft several miles away. We wanted greater range on the next test. Greater range would require greater transmitter power, and could be increased further with a more highly directive antenna to concentrate the energy in a smaller angle. There was then at the Laboratory an excellent curtain array for 28.6 megacycles. It was about 135 feet square and suspended between two steel towers about 250 feet apart. Since it would be easier to get more power at the lower frequency, we decided to use this antenna, and had a new pulse transmitter built at 28.6 megacycles. With the new transmitter more innovations were introduced. A new transmitting tube capable of pulse operation at a much higher anode voltage had become available. Two of these tubes were used in what is called a push-pull circuit. And a new transmitter keying arrangement was found that greatly simplified the generation of very high power pulses of almost any desired length. Ordinarily, keying a very high power pulse transmitter with a multivibrator keyer would require a high power keying circuit which would have to be carefully readjusted every time the transmitter anode voltage was changed. So it was decided to let the radiofrequency transmitting tubes be their own multivibrator keyer;

PLATE I. Radar transmitter used on 28, 50, and 80 megacycles, 1936.

PLATE II. Radar receiver and indicator used on 28, 50, and 80 megacycles, 1936.

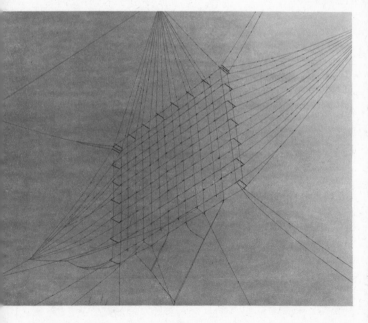

PLATE III. Radar antenna, curtain array type, used on 80 megacycle for both transmitting and receiving, 1936.

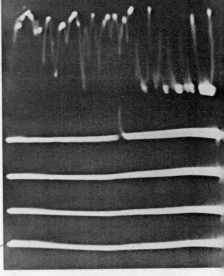

PLATE IV. Echo indications with 80 megacycle radar, 1936. The five range lines represent ten miles each, or fifty miles total. The first ten-mile line is filled with echoes from objects on the ground. The echo from an airplane about fifteen miles away appears on the second line.

PLATE V. Six tube, 15 kilowatt, 200 megacycle oscillator mounted in the XAF radar, 1938.

PLATE VI. XAF radar antenna, curtain array type, on U.S.S. *New York*, shown just below clock, 1938.

such a device would automatically adjust itself to all anode voltages. It is described more fully in Chapter 5. This transmitter was built by R. C. Guthrie, who joined the project in September 1935 and has stayed in radar research and development ever since to become one of the world's leading radar experts.

The tubes used in Guthrie's transmitter were rated by the manufacturer as 100-watt tubes, with a maximum recommended anode voltage of 2.5 kilovolts. In the new pulse transmitter, and with slightly increased filament voltage to enhance the electron supply, we operated the tubes at 15 kilovolts, which was six times their rated voltage. At this time there was no instrument for measuring pulse power, but we could measure pulse length, and this was set to about 5 microseconds. We set the interval between pulses in this transmitter at 269 microseconds, getting thus 3720 pulses per second, and a range interval of approximately 25 miles between pulses. We could measure the average input power, we knew the transmitter to be on 5 microseconds in 269, or about one fiftieth of the time, and we could estimate the tube efficiency. From these data we concluded that the power in the pulse was about 2 to 3 kilowatts.

Synchronizing System

We now had a very satisfactory pulse transmitter, with a highly directive antenna, and a well-designed radar receiver. It was time to put them on the air for another test, to see how well they would work together, and to get a better idea of the distance at which airplanes could be detected. Also the U. S. Navy had been paying our salaries all this time and spending a little additional money now and then on materials and parts for some wild scheme to detect and locate airplanes by radio. If some good progress couldn't be shown pretty soon, we were going to have to drop it and work on something more promising. So again an indicator was improvised and a synchronizing system built to make all parts work together.

The synchronizing system deserves description here, since it was well designed and performed several functions that are employed in some radars of today. The purpose of the synchronizing system is to control the relative timing of transmitted pulses and indicator operation so that time intervals between each transmitted pulse and all its echoes can be determined. This particular one consisted of an oscillator that generated a sine wave at 3720 cycles per second. As may be recognized from our earlier descriptions of oscillating currents in resonant circuits, an oscillating function, such as an alternating electric current or voltage, is a function that repeats a particular sequence of instantaneous amplitude values over and over. The pattern of instantaneous amplitude plotted against time for one whole cycle is called the wave form of the oscillatory function. The cork moved up and down on the surface of the water generates waves that travel in straight lines out from the cork in all directions. If a piece of string (Fig. 19) were floating on the water straight out from the cork in any one direction, and then a picture were taken of the string from one side at the water level, the string would show the hills and valleys that are formed by the

FIG. 19. A cork, c, moved up and down on a water surface will generate waves moving outward in expanding circles. A string, S, on the surface straight out from the cork will show the wave shape.

waves. This hill and valley pattern is the wave form of the oscillation. The wave form of the water waves in this particular case is called a sine wave, because it is the wave form that would be produced if we plotted increasing values of an angle on the horizontal axis, against the values of the sine of the angle on the vertical axis on a piece of plotting paper. In our new system the signal was sent out over two separate circuits, one to the transmitter and one to the indicator. Each circuit contained a phase shifter for adjusting relative phase between transmitted pulse and indicator time base. A phase shifter (Fig. 20) does not change the wave form or frequency of the sine wave, but only advances or retards the whole pattern. It is as if the phase shifter squeezed up or stretched out

FIG. 20. Sine wave retarded by phase shifter. Arrow shows direction and amount of phase shift.

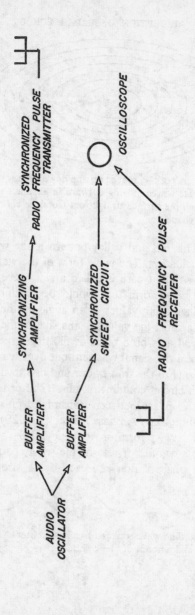

time as the sine wave passed through. Both transmitted pulse and echoes could be moved or positioned on the indicator and lined up with scale or range marks for accurate determination of range to selected targets. Then the keying voltage to the transmitter was distorted from a sine wave to a steep wave front in order to start the transmitter pulse vigorously at exactly the same time in every cycle. The voltage to the indicator was used to trigger the sweep circuit in a cathode ray oscilloscope then commercially available.

As soon as all the components were completed, they were connected together for the test. The transmitter and keying wave form circuits were installed in a small building under the big antenna. The receiver, indicator, and synchronizing oscillator were set up in the main laboratory about 330 yards from the transmitter. The receiving antenna was a horizontal wire half a wavelength long, with a single wire reflector, similar to the antennas used at 60 megacycles in 1934. The 28 megacycle equipment (Fig. 21) was first operated as a complete radar system on April 28, 1936. Echoes were seen almost immediately, and within a few days airplanes were giving excellent echo signals at various distances all the way out to the end of the scale, at 25 miles. There were also many echoes from buildings and other objects on the ground. The echoes were beautifully sharp and clean-cut. There was no smearing out or

---

Fig. 21. Block diagram of radars operated in 1936. The block diagram for the radar tested in December 1934 was similar to this one.

fuzziness, the received pulses were just as short as the sent pulses, and the receiver seemed to recover instantaneously from the transmitted pulse. In fact, the success was so impressive that suddenly everything seemed to happen at once.

For two years, two men—sometimes only one—had struggled along against almost overwhelmingly difficult problems, with much discouragement, and with no evidence of ultimate success except their faith. Then, with the simple throw of a switch, came sudden success, followed by many enthusiastic demonstrations and confidential disclosures to others. A rapidly enlarged team of very competent young engineers was organized, and an immediately expanded program of exploitation of the many possible applications of the new development got under way. But first there were additional problems to solve in order to complete the original development. This was a Navy program. The Navy needed radars to go on ships. But no ship could carry 200-foot antennas spaced 330 yards apart. Antennas would have to be made smaller without loss of directivity, and—most startling of all—wouldn't it be nice if the same antenna could be used for both transmitter and receiver! Although we worked on both these problems, as well as some others, concurrently, we will take them up here one at a time.

CHAPTER 5

RC CIRCUIT MAGIC

In this chapter we shall undertake a more detailed exposition of the technical difficulties overcome in the original development of radar. While the material is very worthwhile for an understanding of radar, it is conceivable that some of you may shy from electricity and electronics. So, if you find yourself less than fascinated after a few paragraphs, you will find that you can skip to Chapter 6 without loss of continuity.

In the title of this chapter R stands for resistance and C for capacitance. As we pursue our little exposition, the aptness of the title will delight us as we watch the electrons rub through resistors and call from condensers the magic of Aladdin's Genie. To understand how a resistor works we must examine the way electrons travel through a conductor.

We may think of a conductor as an open framework of molecules, like the open skeleton of a steel-frame building before any walls are put in. The molecules are so tiny that we cannot see the holes between them, even with a powerful microscope, but still they are there. The electrons, being much smaller than the molecules, can go right through the spaces between them, except at the surface of the conductor, where electrons can easily get in from outside, but can't get out from inside. Electrons inside the conductor can move with lightning speed, but they keep bumping into molecules. In a good conductor the molecules, we might say, are very springy, like live rubber balls, and the electrons bounce right off without losing any speed. Electrons can travel through miles of wire and come out an end connection going almost as fast as when they went in the other end. In a resistor, however, the molecules are not so springy. They are more like leather than live rubber; the electrons lose some speed every time they bump a molecule. After many bumps in traveling through a resistor the electrons come out the end connection going much more slowly than when they went in the other end. The loss in speed means a loss in energy. This energy lost by the electrons is absorbed by the molecules and makes them get warmer. If the bumps come too fast and too hard, the resistor will become hot, and may even melt. In an electric lamp the bumps give just enough energy to keep the filament, which is a resistance wire, glowing white-hot. In a short circuit a very high current flows through the lowered resistance and melts the fuse wire, thus disconnecting the circuit before the whole circuit gets so hot it sets the house on fire.

What we must remember about a resistor is that it is a conductor that has more resistance than what we commonly call a good conductor, but that it does not stop the electrons, or hold them or store them or anything like that. It only slows them down, and it takes longer for a given number of electrons to get through the circuit, or it takes more voltage to drive the electrons at a given rate. The rate of electron flow, or the number of electrons per second going through a circuit, is called the current in the circuit. Current is measured in *amperes*. The force that drives the electrons through a resistor is the *potential difference* across the resistor, or *voltage*, measured in *volts*. As we have seen, the electrons always try to get away from the negative side, where there are too many other electrons, to the positive side, where there is extra room for more electrons. *Resistance* is measured in *ohms*. *One ohm* is that resistance which will allow electrons to get through at the rate of *one ampere* when the voltage across the resistor is *one volt*.

Circuit Components

To return to radar, the resistor in the anode circuit slows down the electrons trying to get to the battery, and allows some of them to go scooting back through the external circuit to hit the grid and turn off the electron stream in the tube. For similar reasons, there must be a resistance, or some equivalent, in the grid circuit between the grid and its bias battery; otherwise the grid voltage could not be changed from the battery voltage, and the valve would be stuck. Since grid current in a radio receiver is usually zero, the grid resistor can be made very high to avoid wasting signal power that is needed for changing grid voltage. It is not unusual for the grid resistor to be a million ohms. The grid resistor is instrumental in "blinding" the receiver after the transmitted pulse, but by itself could do no harm. It is only when associated with a *condenser,* or *capacitor,* that it becomes deadly. A capacitor is a reservoir that has *capacity* for storing electrons. The capacity to store electrons is called *capacitance.*

A capacitor comes closer than anything else I know to fooling the electrons. It consists only of two large sheets of conducting material, like tin foil, with their flat surfaces very close together, but not touching anywhere. When there are more electrons on one sheet than on the other, they can "smell" that there is more room for electrons on the other sheet, and crowding together on the surface facing the other sheet, they try to get across. The closer together the two surfaces, the tighter the electrons crowd trying to get across to the other surface. Most capacitors have a thin sheet of insulation, or non-conducting material, like paper, between the two sheets of tin foil. In addition to allowing the space between surfaces to be very small without shorting, the paper acts as a sort of telescope for the electrons and makes the surfaces look even closer together. The closer together the surfaces look, or the larger the surfaces are, the more electrons will pack themselves in *without changing the potential difference between the two sheets of tin foil.*

Capacity is measured in *farads.* One *farad* is that amount of *capacitance* which will store *one coulomb* of electrical charge when the potential difference across the terminals is *one volt.* It takes 6×10^{18} electrons to make one coulomb of electric charge.

That is 6,000,000,000,000,000,000 electrons. A coulomb is the number of electrons that flow past any point in a circuit in one second when the current is one ampere. A condenser may be charged up merely by connecting a battery across its terminals. When the battery is removed, the charge will remain on the condenser. The voltage across the condenser terminals will remain the same as the battery voltage, and the quantity of charge (number of electrons stored) will depend only on this voltage and the capacitance. If it is a very good condenser, it will hold the charge for many days. Eventually the electrons will "leak" across and discharge the condenser because it is very difficult to keep all surfaces so clean that there is absolutely no leakage anywhere. If a conducting wire is connected across the terminals, the condenser will discharge instantly with a big rush of current through the wire. But when a resistor is connected across the terminals, the condenser will discharge through the resistor at a rate determined by the product of capacitance and resistance. The time in seconds required to discharge a condenser to about one third the starting voltage is equal to the capacitance in farads times the resistance in ohms. This is the *time constant* of the circuit we mentioned some pages back, and the circuit is often referred to as an RC circuit, meaning *r*esistance-*c*apacitance circuit. The conventional symbols for the elements of a circuit are shown in Fig. 22.

The RC circuit will appear again and again in many different roles as the story of radar unfolds. It is what makes the multivibrator work for keying the radar transmitter described in Chapter 3. It is the

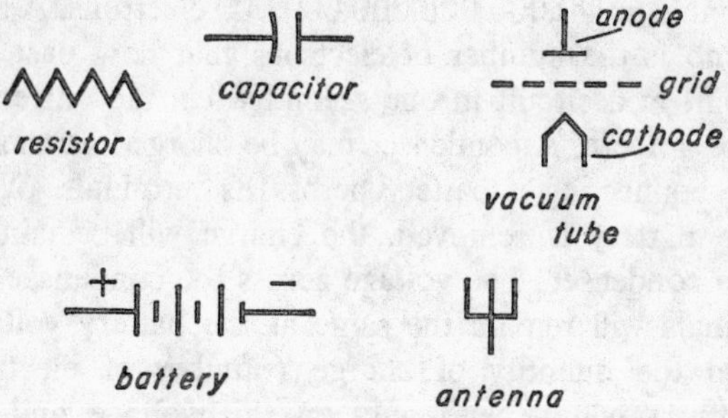

FIG. 22. Radio circuit symbols.

cause of receiver black-out, or blanking, as it is called, after the very strong signals from the transmitter. It is used to make the new transmitter key itself, as we will see later in this chapter. It provides the range scale for radar indicators described in Chapter 8. It enables automatic electrical measurement of range with almost unbelievable precision as told in Chapter 9. It is also important in isolating different parts of the radar receiver from each other to prevent feedback, to be discussed later in this chapter, and it is used in power supplies to reduce hum and noise from the a.c. power lines. So you see, the RC circuit is a very important element in radar. In most of these functions it is associated with a vacuum tube. Usually it controls the action of the grid. I think you will agree that it is worth going to a little trouble to understand how the RC circuit and the vacuum tube react on each other to do so many wonderful things.

Current Flow

Let us think of the grid of a vacuum tube connected to one end of a resistor, the other end of which is connected to the cathode. We call this resistor the grid resistor. As long as no current flows in the resistor, there will be no voltage across the resistor, and the grid will have no bias. In this state the grid will not collect many of the electrons that flow from the cathode to the anode. Now we add the condenser, and connect one condenser plate to the grid, and the other condenser plate to a battery terminal. The other battery terminal goes to the cathode. When the connection is made, current will flow from the battery through the resistor to charge the condenser slowly to the battery voltage. When this is accomplished, the current will stop, there will be no voltage across the resistor, and the grid will have no bias.

Now suppose we change the battery voltage in the negative direction. A current will flow through the resistor until the condenser charge slowly becomes changed to equal the new battery voltage. The voltage across the resistor that makes the current flow becomes a bias on the grid, and the change just made will make that bias negative. As soon as the current in the resistor stops, the bias again becomes zero. If we change the battery voltage in the positive direction, it will result in a positive bias on the grid until the condenser again readjusts its charge to match the battery voltage. But now the grid will collect electrons

93

from the electron stream in the tube. These electrons will go into the condenser and help to charge it to the new battery voltage, so that the current in the resistor, and consequently the bias on the grid, will return to zero more quickly.

Our next experiment (Fig. 23) is to switch the battery voltage rapidly and continuously back and forth between the two voltage values. The current in the resistor will flow first in one direction, then in the other, and the grid bias will alternate between negative and positive, all in unison, or in synchronism with the switching. If the grid collected no electrons from the electron stream in the tube, the total current flowing in one direction in the resistor

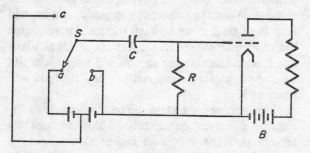

Fig. 23. RC circuit in vacuum tube grid return. Rapid switching of switch *S* between points *a* and *b* generates an alternating current through resistor *R* and an alternating voltage on condenser *C*. Positive peaks of voltage on the vacuum tube grid will draw electrons from the tube into the condenser, and generate a negative bias on the grid as these electrons flow back to the cathode through the resistor. When the switch is connected to point *c*, the negative bias on the grid gradually returns to zero as the condenser discharges through the resistor.

would equal the total current flowing in the opposite direction. This balance would make the average current zero, and consequently the average grid bias zero, and when we stopped switching the battery voltage, the grid bias would very quickly come to rest at zero. But we have seen that when the grid goes positive it collects electrons. These electrons go immediately into the condenser, and then "leak" off more slowly to the cathode through the resistor. This added current in the resistor is always in the same direction, and makes the average bias on the grid become negative. The more negative the average bias, the fewer the electrons collected by the grid during its positive bias swings. The average negative bias will adjust itself automatically until just enough electrons are collected on each positive swing to hold that bias until the next positive swing. Obviously, the greater the voltage swings on the grid from the switching operation, the greater will be the average negative bias. It is very easy to make the voltage swings so great that the average bias is much greater than the cutoff bias, which, as you recall, is the bias that just stops all electron flow in the tube from the cathode to the anode. If, when this happens, we suddenly stop the switching operation and return the battery voltage to a value midway between the two switched valves, the high average negative bias will exist as a charge on the condenser which will slowly "leak" off through the resistor, and permit the negative bias remaining on the grid to return slowly to zero.

The rapidly switched voltage just described is an *alternating voltage,* and the continually reversing current it produced in the resistor is an *alternating current*. Both alternating voltage and alternating current are called signals (Fig. 24). Such signals are usually identified as alternating current signals, or *a.c. signals*. Two reversals constitute one cycle of the signal. The number of cycles per second defines the frequency of the signal. The repeated cycles are called oscillation, and radiofrequency signals are a.c. signals, that oscillate at radiofrequency.

The important things to remember now are these

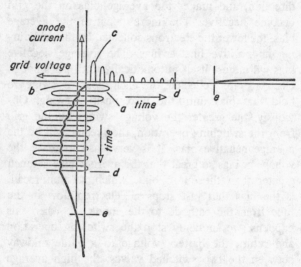

Fig. 24. When the switch of Fig. 23 is replaced by an alternating current signal, the biasing effect is the same. *a* represents the alternating current signal on the grid. *b* represents the resulting average bias due to grid current in the RC circuit. *c* represents the plate current. After termination of signal at time *d*, anode current remains zero until decreasing grid bias reaches cutoff at *e*.

two: (1) When a very high a.c. signal is put on a vacuum tube grid with an RC circuit as described, the average grid bias will be made highly negative, and will require a long time to return to normal when the signal is removed or discontinued, and (2) during the time the grid bias is slowly returning to normal value, the tube current to the anode will be blocked and the tube cannot respond to normal or weak signals.

The Multivibrator in Operation

In Chapter 3 we said that the transmitter was keyed by a multivibrator. It is interesting to see how

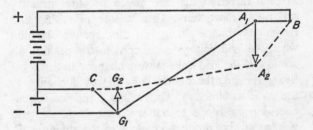

FIG. 25. When a vacuum tube is connected as in Figs. 23 or 26, a change in grid voltage in one direction will produce a change in anode voltage in the opposite direction. The solid line from C to G_1 to A_1 to B represents the potential distribution when the grid is negative at cutoff, anode current is zero and anode voltage is the same as the battery voltage. The dotted line from C to G_2 to A_2 to B represents zero bias on the grid, and high anode current giving rise to a large voltage drop across the anode circuit resistor. Changing grid voltage in the positive direction from G_1 to $_2$ causes a change in anode voltage in the negative direction, from A_1 to $_2$.

RC circuits and vacuum tubes are combined to make a multivibrator. First we examine the effect of a resistor in the anode circuit, connected from the anode to the positive terminal on the supply battery. We call this the anode resistor. If the tube is blocked by negative grid bias so no electrons reach the anode, there will be no current in the anode resistor, therefore no voltage across the resistor, and the anode potential will be the same as the battery potential. Suppose now we change the grid voltage in the positive direction until the bias becomes zero. Then many electrons will flow to the anode, and through the anode resistor to the battery. The voltage across the resistor associated with the current represents a potential difference between the anode and the battery, in such direction that the anode becomes negative relative to the battery. Thus we see (Fig. 25) that the anode voltage changes in the negative direction when the grid voltage is changed in the positive direction. If the grid voltage were changed in the negative direction, the anode voltage would change in the positive direction. Thus when a resistor is connected from anode to battery, changes in the grid voltage always produce changes in the opposite direction in the anode voltage.

A multivibrator (Fig. 26) uses two vacuum tubes, each with its grid returned to cathode through an RC circuit as just described, and its anode connected through an anode resistor to a battery or power supply. The anode of each tube provides the signal for the grid circuit of the other tube. Since the condenser is connected from one anode to the other grid, it is called a coupling condenser. In this circuit,

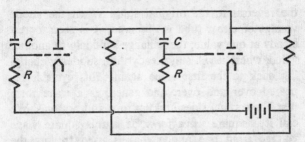

FIG. 26. The basic multivibrator circuit. The output signal at the anode of each tube is connected to the grid of the other tube through an RC circuit.

one tube is always blocked, and the two tubes continually take turns at being blocked. Here is how it works. Let us say that No. 1 tube is blocked, because there is a high negative bias on its grid. The bias comes from a charge on its coupling condenser which is slowly leaking off through its grid resistor, thus slowly returning the grid to zero bias. As the grid passes through cutoff voltage, current starts to flow in tube No. 1, and its anode voltage starts to charge in the negative direction. This causes grid bias in tube No. 2 to change in the negative direction, so the anode in tube No. 2 starts to change in the positive direction. This reversal drives the grid of tube No. 1 further (and faster) in the positive direction and speeds up the change so much that tube No. 2 becomes very quickly blocked, and the grid of tube No. 1 is driven far positive. The electrons it collects charge its coupling condenser so that it quickly settles down to zero bias and waits for the high negative bias on tube No. 2 to drift back through the cutoff voltage in tube No. 2 to initiate

99

the reversal to the original state. When the anode voltage of either tube is observed, it is seen to rest steady at one value, then change suddenly to another value, where it will stay steady until suddenly changing back to the first value again. This cycle is repeated over and over, and generates a wave form that has vertical sides and flat tops and bottoms. We call it a square *wave form*. It is this square wave voltage from one anode that is used to key the transmitter.

We now recall that the transmitter had to be "on" for about 10 microseconds, then "off" for 90 microseconds. The multivibrator keyer had to manage that too. Hence the multivibrator anode that was used to key the transmitter had to stay positive for 10 microseconds and negative for 90 microseconds. This was accomplished by making the multivibrator asymmetric (Fig. 27), that is, making the two RC time constants different. If the anode was to stay positive for 10 microseconds, it had to stay blocked for 10 microseconds. Its RC circuit had to keep its grid biased beyond cutoff for 10 microseconds. Then to make it stay negative for 90 microseconds, the other tube had to be kept blocked for 90 microseconds by its RC circuit, and that is all there was to it.

Let us now get back to the receiver. It is easy to see why the ordinary receiver with large RC circuits connected to the grids would be blind for a while after the powerful pulse from the transmitter. The obvious cure for this condition was circuits designed to have the smallest possible RC time constant in the grid circuit. The acorn-type tube gave the smallest tube capacitance available, enabling the use of small

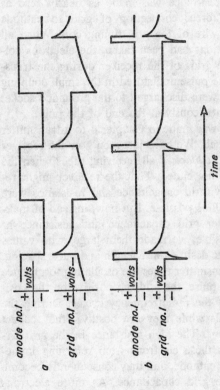

FIG. 27. Voltage waveforms for multivibrator.
(a) Symmetrical multivibrator.
(b) Asymmetrical multivibrator as used to key radar transmitter.

time

anode no.1 — + volts —

grid no.1 — + volts —

a

anode no.1 — + volts —

grid no.1 — + volts —

b

coupling condensers. The tube socket was handmade to get all connections as short as possible. Ingenious circuit designs made the capacitance for storing electrons collected by the grid very small indeed. The grid circuit resistance was made as nearly zero as possible by direct connection of grid to cathode through the wire of the grid tuning coil. When all these precautions had been taken, the electrons collected by the grids of the receiver during the transmission of the pulse and stored in the small coupling capacitances were discharged to the grounded socket almost instantaneously at the end of the pulse.

Reference was made in Chapter 4 to a transmitter that keyed itself. We have just seen how the receiver grids cut off or *blocked* all receiving tubes when the transmitter pulse ended. That the receiver might recover quickly, grid capacitance and resistance were made as small as possible. But now, instead of making transmitter grid capacitance and resistance as small as possible, we made them large, with values to produce the desired pulse length and pulse spacing. When the transmitter tubes are oscillating to produce power in the pulse, the grids go positive on the positive peaks of the radiofrequency cycles. During the short intervals while they are positive, they collect many electrons. The high resistance in the grid circuit prevents these electrons from returning immediately to the cathode, and they consequently become stored in the grid capacitance. As more electrons are stored, the average voltage on the grid becomes more negative. As the average grid voltage becomes more negative, the efficiency of the oscillator at first increases, then decreases very rapidly until oscillation stops. The rate of increase in negative grid voltage depends on grid current and grid circuit capacitance. The desired pulse length is obtained by proper selection of this capacitance. If anode voltage is increased, grid current during oscillation will increase, but so will the negative voltage required to terminate the pulse. These two effects just balance, and the pulse length stays constant as anode voltage is changed. When oscillation stops at the end of the pulse, the capacitance then discharges relatively slowly through the grid circuit resistance, thus restoring conditions for generating the next pulse. If the grid circuit resistor were connected directly to the cathode, the next pulse would start spontaneously when the negative grid voltage became sufficiently small to allow oscillations to start. Since it was desirable, however, to keep the starting time of the pulse completely under the control of a remotely supplied synchronizing signal, the grid resistor was returned to a negative voltage supply set just high enough to prevent the start of oscillation. The grid resistance then had a value that would permit the grid voltage to recover very nearly to this supply value in a time a little shorter than the spacing between the pulses. There it would rest until the synchronizing signal further reduced the negative bias on the grid and so let the next pulse start.

In Chapter 9 we will have use for a delayed pulse generator (Fig. 28). Such a generator gives a pulse output following an input or "trigger" pulse by a controlled time interval. It can be used as a precise time-measuring circuit, as required for very accurate

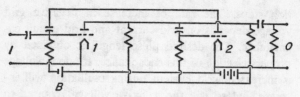

FIG. 28. Basic circuit for delayed pulse generator. This is similar to the multivibrator in principle. Grid No. *1* is biased just beyond cutoff by battery *B*, to prevent self-oscillation. Grid No. 2 is returned to a high positive bias to increase the slope of the discharge voltage curve where it crosses the cutoff bias, and so provide a more positive and stable delay termination. The trigger pulse is introduced at *I*, and the delayed output pulse is obtained at *O*.

measurement of range. A multivibrator may be modified to perform this function. Let the grid of tube No. 1 be returned through its resistor to a fixed negative bias slightly greater than cutoff. This will keep the multivibrator from oscillating, since tube No. 1 will always stay blocked. A positive trigger pulse applied to this grid so as to drive it through the cutoff bias will start current flow in tube No. 1. Tube No. 2 will block instantly, then after a time determined by the RC circuit in the grid of tube No. 2, tube No. 1 will block and stay blocked. The act of shifting the blocked condition from tube No. 2 to tube No. 1 generates an output pulse. This output pulse follows the trigger pulse by a time interval that is directly proportional to the RC product in the grid circuit of tube No. 2. If the resistance, R, is a variable resistance, the time interval between the trigger pulse and the output pulse can be adjusted by adjusting the resistance value of R (Fig. 29).

104

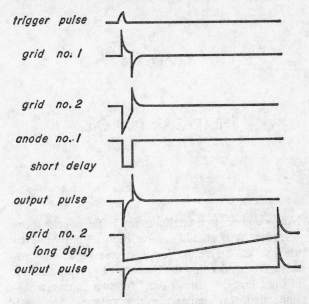

trigger pulse

grid no. 1

grid no. 2

anode no. 1

short delay

output pulse

grid no. 2
long delay

output pulse

FIG. 29. Voltage waveforms of delayed pulse generator. The same circuit also serves as a linear sweep generator for a radar range line. In this application the output is taken from grid No. 2. Linearity is due to the high positive return for grid No. 2. See also Fig. 37.

And there in brief, for the benefit of the technically minded, are the secrets of RC time constants. Now let us return to a more dramatic theme.

105

CHAPTER 6

THE RADAR DUPLEXER

Now we come to a vital question in the development of radar. Why should it have been so important to use the same antenna for both transmitter and receiver? Consider first the problem of synchronization of direction, or "team work," for two antennas. Assume that two similar directive antennas are used, one for the transmitter and one for the receiver. It would then be necessary that both antennas point always in exactly the same direction. But in practice one could not always be sure that both antennas were pointed in exactly the same direction, especially while being rotated, and if either antenna were just slightly off direction, the sensitivity of the system would be reduced, and determination of true direction to the target made more difficult. With a single antenna, there would be no question whether transmitter and receiver were accurately turned in the same direction. But suppose that the two antennas were put side by side on the same rotating platform. We now consider the matter of gain in sensitivity and directivity. If the space occupied by the two antennas were used for one antenna on the transmitter, the illumination energy on the target would be doubled, and directivity would be increased, or, to say it differently, the beam would be sharpened. But if this same large antenna were used on the receiver, the receiver beam would be sharpened in the same way, and the sensitivity of the receiver would be doubled. So the whole effect of replacing the two equal antennas by one as large as the two together for both transmitter and receiver (Fig. 30) would be to make the system four times as powerful (or sensitive) and make the beam four

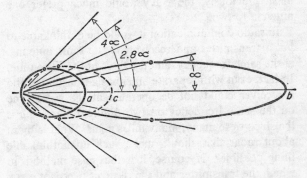

FIG. 30. Comparison of effective azimuth patterns of radar beams, *a*, with two equal antennas side by side, one for transmitting and the other for receiving, and, *b*, with the two connected together as one antenna used both for transmitting and receiving. These are effective power curves. It is noted that *b* has four times the effective power on axis as *a*, while *a* has four times the effective angular spread in azimuth, as indicated by the angles $\propto$ and $4\propto$. *c* indicates the increase in radar range over *a*. Since radar range is proportional to the fourth root of effective power, *c* is the fourth root of *b*, or 1.4 times *a*.

times as sharp in one coordinate. This would be a very worthwhile gain.

There was yet another reason in the Navy for a single antenna. Ships are crowded vehicles. There is little room for big antennas. When a new radar antenna is put on a ship, usually something else has to come off. Also ships are expected to float right side up, and if one should turn over and float upside down, it would not be considered an unqualified success. Too much weight at the top of the mast would tend to make the ship capsize. But to see all around radar antennas should be as high as possible on the mast. Obviously, the Navy would much prefer one antenna to two.

In radio communication it would be unthinkable to put a transmitter and receiver on the same antenna, at the same frequency, and use them at the same time. In fact, even with separate antennas a transmitter and a receiver could not be operated at the same time on the same frequency on two different ships unless the ships were many, many miles apart. What is there about radar that should make such an unthinkable thing possible? Of course, it is the pulse method, in which the transmitter and the receiver need not operate at exactly the same time. When the transmitter is sending the pulse, the receiver does not need to be receiving echoes, and when the receiver is receiving echoes, the transmitter can be completely silent. Since it is all so simple, it should be easy, but let's see. What problems had to be solved in order to connect the same antenna to transmitter and receiver?

In the first place, as just pointed out, transmitter and receiver are on exactly the same frequency and have the same bandwidth and cannot be isolated from each other with frequency filters. And since the antenna must be connected to the *output* of the transmitter and the *input* of the receiver, just connecting them all together willy-nilly would be connecting the highest energy point in the system directly to the lowest energy point in the system, and that would make more problems. It would be like putting all the power of a great hydroelectric generating plant into one little flashlight lamp. The mistreated flashlight would go up in smoke. And that is about what would happen to the radar receiver, too. So if there was to be any receiver left after the first pulse went out, it was necessary to prevent energy from the transmitter from ever reaching the receiver input. Also, if part of the transmitter energy was spent in burning up the receiver, there would be less energy left to illuminate the target. When you want to get as much energy as possible on the target, it would be foolish to waste part of it burning up receivers. Further, if transmitter and receiver were connected together while echoes were being received, some of the echo signal might get lost in the transmitter circuits and never get to the receiver at all. The only answer to all these problems is to disconnect the receiver while transmitting, and disconnect the transmitter while receiving. All that is needed is a switch that will connect the antenna to the transmitter alone for sending out the pulse, and then reconnect it to the receiver alone for receiving echoes. Surely this should be simple enough.

The Purpose of a Duplexer

The switch has to be in the antenna connecting circuit, which is for very high radiofrequencies. The procedure therefore is not quite the same as connecting batteries to operate a light or a little motor. Such things as size and shape of conductors, spacings, and insulators, perfect electrical contact at critical spots and no contact at other spots, all these become important factors. But these things seem easy until we see how fast the switch must operate. The switch must be on the transmitter side for just 5 microseconds, then on the receiver side for a much longer time, and, remember, a microsecond is one millionth of a second! But the much longer time is still only one fourth of a thousandth of a second. Not only that; the switch is supposed to throw from the transmitter side to the receiver side in no time at all, when a millionth of a second is a significant length of time. Furthermore, the switch would have to repeat the whole switching cycle from transmitter to receiver and back to transmitter again four thousand times a second. It did not look possible for any kind of mechanical switch with moving parts. The only kind of electrical conductors that could move fast enough for such a switch would be electrons or ions. Ions come from gas, and are produced by electrifying the gas.

The first solution for this problem used electrons for switching, and the switch was called a *duplexer*, meaning a device for duplex operation of the antenna —duplex referring to two uses, one for transmitting and one for receiving. To understand how to switch a radar antenna with electrons, we will have to take another little excursion into the field of resonant circuits.

Do you remember that we described the radiating element in a radio antenna as a piece of wire one half wavelength long? When radiofrequency energy is fed to such a wire at just the right frequency, electrons in the wire bounce back and forth between the two ends of the wire, and radiate electromagnetic energy into space on the same frequency. Such a piece of wire is a resonant circuit that loses a considerable part of its energy by radiation on each cycle. It therefore has high radiation loss, and subsequently relatively low Q. Suppose now we take such a piece of wire and bend it at the center until it is doubled like a hair pin, with the two sides parallel and fairly close together. Electrons still will follow the wire around the bend, and bounce back and forth between the ends just as if the wire were straight. But now the electrons in the two sides of the "hair pin" or *line*, as we will call it, will be moving in opposite directions, and the radiation from one side will be just opposite to the radiation from the other side. Since these two separate radiations will always be equal and opposite, they tend to cancel each other with the result that there will be practically no radiation at all. We still have a resonant circuit, and it is still at very nearly the same frequency, but since it does not radiate appreciably, we say the radiation loss is very small, and the circuit has a high Q. Thus a quarter wavelength of two-wire radiofrequency transmission line shorted at one end and open at the other end is a high Q

resonant circuit. Such a circuit has an important property. Even though the direct current resistance may be almost zero, the two wire ends at the open end of the line act at resonant frequency as if they were the terminals of a very high resistance, sometimes as high as many millions of ohms of resistance. In fact, a lower direct current resistance through the wire will in general produce a higher resonant frequency resistance across the ends of the wire. An explanation of this curious fact is the first step in understanding how the radar duplexer works.

Have you ever looked carefully at the lead-in connection from an FM radio or television set to its antenna? Usually it is a flat strip of plastic with a wire embedded along each edge. This is a two-wire transmission line for conducting radiofrequency energy from one place to another, such as TV signals from the antenna to the TV set. The voltage at any point on one conductor of this line will oscillate at the frequency of the energy flowing on the line. At the same position on the line but on the other conductor the same oscillating voltage will occur, but displaced in time by one half cycle of the radiofrequency energy. Being one half cycle apart in time, they are opposite in phase; when one is positive, the other is negative. Radiation from the two wires thus tends to cancel and radiofrequency energy can be conducted for considerable distance with negligible radiation loss.

Now suppose that one conductor of a quarter-wave resonant line be connected at its open end to one side of a two-wire transmission line on which energy is flowing with the same frequency to which the resonant line is tuned. Electrons at this junction point corre-

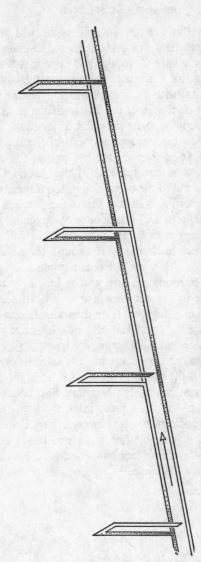

FIG. 31. The open ends of a quarter-wave line shorted at one end may be connected directly across a radiofrequency transmission line with negligible effect on the line at resonant frequency.

sponding to the voltage at that point will travel around the resonant line and arrive at the other end just half a cycle later. A voltage will appear at the unconnected end of the resonant line, and this voltage will be identical with the voltage which appears at the same instant on the other conductor of the transmission line directly opposite the point of junction. Since the voltages on the unconnected end of the resonant line and at that position on the transmission line are identical, the unconnected end of the resonant line can be connected to the other side of the transmission line, and no current will flow across the junction. Instead, the electrons will just bounce back again to the first side to repeat the cycle. The electrons will continue to bounce back and forth around the resonant line, always meeting an equivalent number of electrons in the transmission line, and as long as there is no resistance in the resonant line to absorb energy, there will be no energy lost from the transmission line. Thus we have the open end of a quarter-wave resonant line connected right across the transmission line (Fig. 31), and all the energy in the transmission line goes right past the resonant line as if it were not there at all. In other words, the resonant line connected this way looks like an almost infinitely high resistance. This condition exists, however, only if the resistance in the resonant line is so small that essentially all the electrons from one side get across to the other side on each cycle.

Resistance Inversion

Now suppose we insert a small resistance in place of the short circuit at the end of the quarter-wave resonant line away from the transmission line. Electrons bouncing from one side of the resonant line to the other now must flow through this resistance, and some of their energy will be absorbed. Consequently, the voltage appearing in the resonant line at the points of junction with the transmission line will not quite equal the voltage in the transmission line, and some energy will be absorbed from the transmission line. Now the resonant line still looks like a high resistance across the transmission line, but not quite as high as before. If the resistance at the far end is increased, still more energy will be absorbed from the transmission line and the resonant line will look like a still lower resistance across the transmission line. Now we can see that increasing a real resistance at one end of a quarter-wave resonant line has the effect of decreasing the apparent resistance at the other end of the resonant line (Fig. 32). This is called impedance inversion, and is a very important property of a quarter-wave resonant line. It is also an essential operation in a radar duplexer.

If we keep on decreasing the apparent resistance at the junction points by increasing the real resistance at the far end of the quarter-wave line, we will reach a point where the real resistance at one end and the apparent resistance at the other end are equal. The value of resistance that produces this result defines a

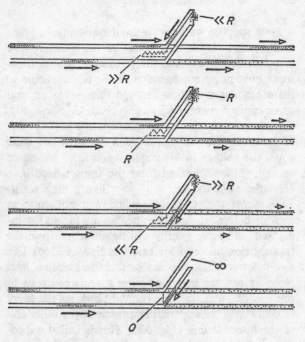

FIG. 32. A quarter-wave line connected across a radio-frequency transmission line will act as a short circuit across the line at resonant frequency when the remote end of the quarter-wave line is open. When the remote end is terminated in a real resistor, *decreasing* the *real* resistance will have the effect of *increasing* the *apparent* resistance across the transmission line.

very important property of transmission lines in general. It is called the characteristic impedance of the line. For a two-wire transmission line the characteristic impedance depends only on the ratio of wire diameter to spacing between wires, and is the same for all frequencies, so long as the spacing between wires is a very small fraction of a wavelength. A resistance that is equal to the characteristic impedance of the line, when connected across the end of the line, will absorb all the energy flowing along the line without reflecting or bouncing any electrons back along the line. When a transmission line is thus terminated in its characteristic impedance, it is said to be *matched* to the load. This is the condition for maximum transfer of power from the line to the load. If the terminating resistance is any other value, some of the electrons flowing along the line will bounce back along the line. If the terminating resistance is lower than the characteristic impedance, some electrons flowing along one side of the line will get through the resistance and come back on the other side of the line. If the resistance is higher than the characteristic impedance, some of the electrons will bounce back along the same side on which they came.

Now we can tell what will happen when we make the resistance at the far end of our quarter-wave line larger than the characteristic impedance of the line. Some of the electrons will bounce back along the same side on which they came, and when they get back to the junction point with the transmission line, they will produce a voltage of opposite sign to the voltage in the transmission line. The result will be just the same as if part of the voltage from the other side of the transmission line had got across to the first side. And this is just what would happen if a resistance smaller than the characteristic impedance of the line had been connected directly across the transmission line at its points of junction with the quarter-wave line. Further increase in the real resistance at the far end of the quarter-wave line would look like further decrease in apparent resistance across the junction points. Ultimately, if the remote ends are left disconnected entirely, which is the same as connecting them with an infinitely high resistance, the resulting apparent resistance across the junction points will be infinitely low, or equivalent to a short circuit. Now we have discovered another very curious property of a quarter-wave line. If we connect the two wire ends at one end of the quarter-wave line to the two sides of a two-wire transmission line and leave the two wires open at the other end of the quarter-wave line, it will have the same effect at resonant frequency as connecting a short circuit right across the transmission line, even though there is no metallic connection at all between the two sides of the line. This peculiar property is also used in the radar duplexer.

The First Duplexer

The first radar duplexer looked very simple for the switching function it performed. As stated earlier, it used electrons for switching (Fig. 33). The switching electrons flowed from cathode to grid in the receiver input tubes. The receiver input stage used two tubes

118

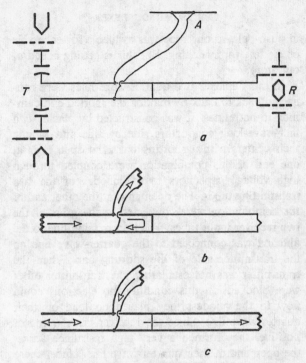

FIG. 33. The first radar duplexer switched with electrons in the grid circuit of the receiver input tubes.

(a) A half wavelength, two-wire line is shorted at the center, terminated in the transmitter output at T and in the receiver input at R. The antenna, A, is connected through a transmission line to the proper impedance point on the transmitter side of the half-wave line.

(b) During transmission of the pulse, the receiver resistance is very low, so very little of the transmitter power gets to the receiver, and the transmitter is matched to the antenna for good power transfer.

(c) During reception the receiver resistance is high and the transmitter resistance is much higher, so the two quarter-wave lines are tightly coupled through the common shorting bar at the center. The antenna is matched through the resonant lines for good signal transfer to the receiver.

in push-pull, so one tube was available for each side of the line for switching. But this is getting ahead of our story.

In this duplexer two quarter-wave lines were connected back to back by making the shorted end common to both lines. It was constructed by placing two half-wave-long conductors side by side and joining their centers with a shorting bar. The open ends at one end of this combination were coupled through high voltage capacitors to the anodes of the two transmitting tubes. The open ends at the other end of the combination were connected to the grids of the two receiver input tubes. The transmission line to the antenna was connected to the quarter-wave line on the transmitter side of the shorting bar. When the transmitter was not oscillating, the transmitter tubes were blocked. In this condition no electrons could flow to the anodes; they placed no load on their quarter-wave line. Since the receiver grids were not positive, they formed a very high resistance across the open end of their quarter-wave line. Under these conditions the two quarter-wave lines were tightly coupled at the common shorting bar, so that any voltage fed to either one would appear alike on both. Thus any signal picked up by the antenna and fed through the transmission line to the transmitter side of this duplexer would appear at the receiver input grids to be amplified by the receiver and displayed by the indicator. The transmitter would absorb none of this energy, since it introduced no resistance into the circuit.

When the transmitter was turned on to send a pulse, it changed everything. The receiver grids,

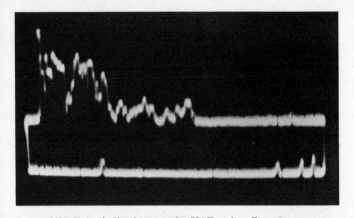

PLATE VII. Echo indications on the XAF radar. Zero range occurs at the top, left, where the transmitted signal (highest vertical line) appears. Range increases to the right on the top line, and to the left on the bottom line, 25 nautical miles on each line. About 12 miles of ground-based objects appear, together with a weak airplane echo at 21 miles, a group of three airplane echoes between 25 and 31 miles, and one at 43 miles.

PLATE VIII. Model XAF radar, left, built by the U.S. Naval Research Laboratory in 1938, and its production version, the model CXAM, right, built by the Radio Corporation of America, in 1940. The U.S. Navy purchased 20 CXAM sets, all of which were delivered prior to December 1941.

PLATE IX. Four tube, 330 kilowatt radar oscillator, tuneable from 180 to 220 megacycles, developed by the U.S. Naval Research Laboratory for the SC-1 and SK radar series. The General Electric Co. produced about 500 radar sets for the U.S. Navy based on this design.

PLATE X. Twelve tube, one million watt, 200 megacycle radar oscillator, developed and used in 1941 by the U.S. Naval Research Laboratory for testing high-power radiofrequency components for radar.

PLATE XI. Six tube oscillator developed for airborne radar use. This oscillator developed 60 kilowatts at 500 megacycles, or 50 kilowatts at 600 megacycles. A two tube version giving 20 kilowatts at 500 megacycles was used for the ASB radar transmitter. Twenty-six thousand sets using this oscillator were produced during World War II by Bendix Radio Co., R.C.A. Manufacturing Co., and Westinghouse Electric and Manufacturing Co.

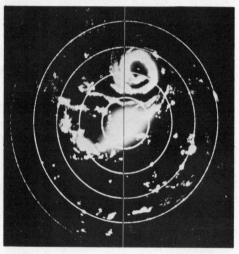

PLATE XII. Microwave P.P.I. presentation of a storm front and a hurricane. The circles are range indicators at 20 mile intervals. The dark vertical line through the center is a north-south line. The white areas represent rainfall. A heavy storm front appears as a fat line through the radar location at the center from SW to NE. The spiral outline of a hurricane is shown just to the east of north with its center 45 miles from the radar. Between the hurricane and the main storm front are several secondary storm fronts, appearing as irregular lines of light. Scattered local showers are shown for nearly 100 miles in all directions.

driven positive, collected many electrons from their cathodes and became a relatively low resistance across the open ends of the receiving quarter-wave line. This real resistance appeared by impedance inversion as a high resistance across the shorting bar. But since the resistance of the shorting bar itself is always nearly zero, almost all the energy flowing through the shorting bar would stay on the transmitter side, and very little would go into the receiving side to be lost in the receiver. This process would protect the receiver from being burned up by the high transmitter power, for the more power absorbed by the receiver, the lower would be the input resistance and the smaller proportion of the total power would get to the receiver. This explains how the receiver becomes effectively disconnected during transmission of the pulse.

But what happens to the transmitter energy? The quarter-wave frame coupled to the transmitter, being shorted at the far end, itself looks like an infinitely high resistance across the transmitter output; it absorbs only enough power to keep the receiver input resistance low. But the transmission line to the antenna is also connected across this line, and it is not resonant but is matched to the antenna at its other end. It therefore shows its own characteristic impedance to the transmitter resonant line, and conducts all the transmitter power to the antenna.

You can see that the radar duplexer was quite an ingenious device. Normally it kept the antenna connected to the receiver and lost no signal in the transmitter. It required no special operation to switch the antenna from the receiver to the transmitter for sending out the pulse. The transmitter pulse itself caused the antenna to "let go" the receiver and "grab hold" of the transmitter, but only for so long as the pulse was being sent out. As soon as the transmitter stopped sending the pulse, the antenna dropped it and "hooked up" to the receiver again—all in a split microsecond! Later, when frequencies were made higher and power was much increased, the switching power absorbed by the receiver input grids became too much for them, in spite of the duplexer protection. It then became necessary to use specially designed gas discharge tubes instead of the receiver input grids. The discharge tubes (Fig. 34) worked in the same manner as the receiver input grids, except that they switched with ions instead of electrons, and lower shorting resistance and higher open circuit resistance could be developed. This arrangement gave much better switching efficiency at high power levels, and became standard practice in all radar duplexers.

The duplexer just described was first built and tested in the summer of 1936. It worked perfectly the first time it was tried, and its success leads me to something that has been a significant part of all my research. Back in Chapter 1, I said that I believed that some new ideas appear as if by accident, containing something more than existed in prior knowledge. Dr. Taylor, head of the Radio Division, had said we ought to try using a single antenna, since transmitter and receiver did not have to be operating simultaneously. I had said it was impossible, because, if for no other reason, the receiver would be burned up by the transmitter. Leo Young, my immediate supervisor, then asked me if I could not use some arrange-

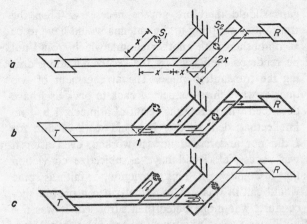

FIG. 34. The high power duplexer switches with ions in the gas discharge tubes, S_1 and S_2.

(a) In the basic circuit, x is one quarter wavelength.

(b) In the receiving condition, S_1 and S_2 are open, so energy from the antenna is reflected back at t and all goes into the receiver R.

(c) In the transmitting condition, S_1 and S_2 are closed, so energy from the transmitter, T, is reflected at r, and all goes out the line to the antenna.

ment of tuned circuits with spark gaps to protect the receiver. It was obvious that I had to try something.

I did not understand impedance inversion at the time, although I had heard that there was such a thing. I knew, however, that the input impedance of vacuum tubes was high when grids were negative, and low when they were positive. So I figured that if they were matched by a high impedance circuit for the negative condition, when they were driven positive they would be so badly mismatched that very little of the input energy would be absorbed. Spark

123

gaps should therefore not be necessary. Then the transmitter coupling to the antenna would have to be accomplished with another circuit, which would not be rendered inefficient by the receiver loading during the transmitted pulse. The arrangement of two quarter-wave lines connected back to back as I have described was purely the result of a hunch. I had no intellectual idea whether it would work or not, for I did not understand how it worked, even after it was successful. I did have a subjective conviction that it would work. This conviction, or faith as some would call it, was so strong that when it proved successful I was more elated than surprised. It was not until many years afterward, when several other people were claiming invention of the radar duplexer and everyone had a different explanation of its operation, that I was forced to give a rigorous explanation of how it did work. Then for the first time I think I began really to understand it. Then it appeared that the original form in which I first tried it was the most simple, most direct, and, for the frequencies used, most efficient design I could have made. It was referred to by patent attorneys as one of those rare cases of "flash of genius" when something really new and basic appears. But in all sincerity I can take no personal credit for it, because I did not create it. I only followed a "hunch," or, as I prefer to call it, an inspiration, in which the completed configuration appeared in my imagination without an understanding of how it worked, but with a feeling of great confidence that it would work. It was as if a source of knowledge out of this world had momentarily been opened to me, and I was guided by it. This is but one of many such experiences that have marked my professional career. Do you wonder that my faith in Divine Providence is both profound and precious?

CHAPTER 7

RADAR FOR SHIPS

Invention of the radar duplexer solved the problem of a single antenna for both transmitting and receiving. This was the first great step toward putting radar on ships. The next problem was to make the antenna smaller without losing directivity, or beam sharpness. Radio antenna directivity is determined by the dimensions of the antenna in wavelengths. An antenna four wavelengths on a side will have a beam about 20 degrees wide, regardless of frequency. Our 28.6 megacycle antenna was four wavelengths on a side, or about 135 feet square. For shipboard use we wanted the antenna to be less than 20 feet square, but still have a beam not more than 20 degrees wide. The wavelength would have to be under five feet, in order to get four wavelengths within 20 feet. We chose a frequency of 200 megacycles to work on, giving a wavelength of about 58 inches.

The First "Sea-Going" Radar

Mr. Arthur A. Varela joined the radar group on May 8, 1936. His first task was development of a

200 megacycle radar transmitter. In those days 200 megacycles a second was almost too high a frequency to think about. Transmitting tubes for this frequency were virtually unknown. But if one used high voltages for pulsing, tubes could be made to do things that their manufacturers never dreamed of. Varela, using some experimental high frequency Western Electric tubes designed for 1250 volts on the anode, got some quite respectable pulse power at 200 megacycles with about 7½ kilovolts on the anodes. A frequency converter was built to amplify the 200 mc radar echo signals and convert them to the receiver frequency, which had been changed from 28.6 to 80 mcs. A small 200 mc antenna was built, only about 10 feet square. When these units were all assembled with a duplexer, they worked well enough to encourage us to put the whole 200 mc system on a ship for a test at sea. The Navy made the destroyer *Leary* available for this purpose. The antenna was fastened to the barrel of a 5-inch gun so it could be trained and elevated. The equipment was mounted in packing boxes on the open deck, and protected from the weather with tarpaulins. Connecting wires and radiofrequency transmission lines were strung in the open. It was probably as crude an assemblage of motley electronic gear as ever operated on a Navy ship.

The morning of departure from the Washington Navy Yard was preceded by a night of heavy rain and east winds which combined with a high tide to flood the Navy Yard piers. Special gangplanks had to be swung out over the water to get us aboard. It was as if all the elements of nature were combining to celebrate the event. So unusual a spectacle did it present, with a paved street running right into the water, as if to carry land traffic under the destroyer, that I yielded to the temptation to sneak an illegal picture of the scene. I got a perfect shot of the destroyer and the flooded street, with a prize-winning composition. At least, I'm sure it would have won prizes had I remembered to remove the camera lens cap!

It was in April 1937 when we sailed down the Potomac River on the U.S.S. *Leary* with the first "seagoing" radar. For the first time we observed how all the land seemed to be moving on the radar indicator as the ship carried the radar along. It was interesting also to observe how prominent objects, such as water towers, bridges, and tall buildings, could be identified on the radar. But especially interesting was the way in which other ships showed up as strong radar targets standing out by themselves with nothing but "empty" water all around them. We learned a lot about radar on the ocean during these tests, and we also learned that we didn't get seasick quite so easily if we lay on our backs in our bunks. But one thing became painfully evident. Before radar could do all that was desired of it on Navy ships, it would have to be much more sensitive to distant aircraft targets. This set did not see any airplanes farther away than 16 miles. A larger antenna and a more powerful transmitter would be needed. The larger antenna required no further research. The more powerful transmitter was quite another story.

A More Powerful Transmitter

We move ahead now to the summer of 1937. Pulse radar had been operating with phenomenal success for over a year at the Naval Research Laboratory. Sets had been built and operated successfully at 28.6, 50, 80, and 200 megacycles. Many demonstrations had been given to high officials of the Government, and the Navy and the Army. The basic designs had been given to the Army's Signal Corps Laboratories, and they were hard at work developing them for their particular needs. The immediate Navy problem was to get higher power pulses at 200 mcs.

In Chapter 3 we pointed out that the time required for electrons to get through a vacuum tube limited the high frequency at which the tube could work. To reach higher frequencies required shortening of distances between cathode and grid. Higher anode voltages to make the electrons travel faster could partly compensate for greater distances between grid and anode, but there was no way to avoid putting the grid and cathode very close together. This configuration gave rise to many tube manufacturing problems, all combining to limit high frequency transmitting tubes to very small sizes. If more power were to be generated, some way would have to be found to get more tubes into the oscillator circuit. The two tube push-pull circuit was in common use. It was known that tubes could be connected in parallel without limit except as to upper frequency of operation. For example, more power output from an audiofrequency amplifier could be obtained using two tubes in parallel on each side of a push-pull circuit, making four tubes in all. This was no help to us, however, because when we put tubes in parallel with circuits known at that time, the combination could be made to operate only at lower frequencies. The first idea was to take two push-pull oscillators and connect them together in such a way that any two adjacent tubes were connected in a complete push-pull circuit. This arrangement resulted actually in four complete push-pull circuits for four tubes, with each tube connected to two circuits. This apparatus worked without lowering the frequency at which the tubes could operate, but all four tubes could not be made to work evenly. Some would get red-hot while others ran cool. Then it was decided that we had more circuits than we needed to connect the tubes together. So half the circuits were eliminated.

Let us number the tubes 1, 2, 3, and 4. In a push-pull oscillator circuit a resonant circuit is used to connect the two anodes, one anode at each end of the circuit. Another resonant circuit connects the grids in like manner. At 200 mcs quarter-wave lines were used as resonant circuits, with one vacuum tube connected to each side of the line at the open ends. To eliminate half the circuits from our four-tube oscillator, one resonant circuit was connected between the anodes of tubes 1 and 2, one circuit between the anodes of tubes 3 and 4, one circuit between the grids of tubes 2 and 3, and one circuit between the grids of tubes 4 and 1. We then had four tubes all connected together in push-pull circuits, but all four were really in series in the oscillating circuit, although they were

130

not in a multi-stage amplifier connection. The circuit forced all tubes to operate at the same radiofrequency voltages; they had to share the load equally and all work alike. It proved to be highly successful.

The Ring Oscillator Circuit

Such a circuit is not limited to four tubes. It only is necessary that the number of tubes be even. This follows from the symmetry of the circuit. As the number of tubes is increased, however, other difficulties arise. It was found that six tubes (Fig. 35) were very stable, but eight tubes tended to divide up in groups of tubes on other frequencies. Development was concentrated therefore on a six-tube oscillator, which came to be known as the ring oscillator circuit, since the tubes were mounted in a ring.

The ring oscillator circuit proved to be remarkably stable and versatile. In the laboratory it was built with many different types of tubes, with numbers ranging from 4 to 18 tubes, at frequencies from 100 to 600 mcs, and pulse power levels from a few watts to a megawatt. The first oscillator to produce a million watts of pulse power was a 12-tube ring oscillator at 200 mcs, built at NRL in 1941. The Navy purchased nearly a thousand radar sets using a 200 mc, 330 kw four-tube ring oscillator developed at NRL, and the U. S. Army Signal Corps adopted the device for the 205 mc 16-tube oscillator in the SCR 268, of which over 500 were purchased.

The next problem was selection of a tube suitable for high voltage pulsing at 200 mcs. Since the upper

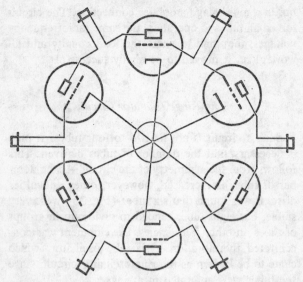

Fig. 35. Six-tube ring circuit oscillator used in radar model XAF.

frequency limit could be raised by increasing voltage, and the largest possible tube was needed, tests were made with tubes that could not quite reach 200 mcs at normal voltages. At this point in the work another unrelated development came to our rescue. A small vacuum tube company in San Bruno, California, had been trying to develop transmitting tubes that would "stand up" in amateur radio use. Radio amateurs were notorious for overworking radio transmitting tubes and then complaining to the tube manufacturers when the tubes "melted in fervent heat." This company had just brought out a vacuum tube that could work at 2.5 kv with the anodes red-hot, and keep right on working even when the anodes became white-hot and the operator could read his log in their light. Although these tubes were considerably larger than any 200 mc tubes available, they could be made to oscillate at very nearly 200 mcs with normal voltages. When a six-tube ring oscillator was designed for these tubes at 200 mcs and they were pulsed in it at high voltage, it worked like a charm. We found that with a 10 to 20 per cent increase in filament voltage the anodes could be operated at 15 kv to produce ten to fifteen kw of power at 200 mc. This was more pulse power than we had ever had, even at 28.6 mcs. We achieved it in February 1938. The following weeks saw this oscillator incorporated into a new radar setup with a rotatable antenna about 20 feet square.

Operation of this radar in the summer of 1938 equaled our dreams when it tracked a small observation plane of wood and fabric construction to a distance of more than a hundred miles! Radar was now ready for regular Navy sea-going equipment. In March of 1938 a project was started in the Laboratory with this objective. H. E. Reppert was the design engineer chosen to take the electrical circuits and components strung together on laboratory benches to test the new 200 mc radar and mold them together into a well-designed piece of radio equipment that would operate reliably on shipboard, even under shock of gunfire. The resulting radar, designated the model XAF, was installed on the battleship *New York* in December 1938 and tested at sea during January, February, and March 1939. The success of these tests was so spectacular that production for

Navy use was ordered at once. The commercial production of this set, designated model CXAM, was almost an exact copy of the XAF. Twenty sets were purchased, nineteen of which were installed on ships and in service when war broke out with Japan, in 1941. These were the only radars in service in the Navy at this time. They carried the main burden of enemy aircraft detection and friendly aircraft direction until supplemented by the model SK three years later. The SK, which also operated on 200 mcs, was a further outgrowth of the NRL radar work. The XAF-CXAM-SK series of radars together constitute a story by themselves, a story which we will reserve for some future time.

CHAPTER 8

RANGE INDICATORS

When most people talk about radar they think of the radar "screen," the indicator that displays echo signals. There are many types of radar indicators in use today. But in 1936 it was necessary to develop one for 28.6 mc radar. It is interesting to contemplate just what this instrument had to do.

The transmitter was sending out 3720 pulses per second. Following each pulse signal, a scattered succession of echo signals was received before the next pulse was sent out. Each signal had a duration of 5 microseconds, and one sometimes occurred close enough to overlap another. The indicator had to display all these pulses in a pattern, had to present each transmitted pulse and all echoes received from it in proper time relationships, and repeat the whole pattern 3720 times a second in exactly the same place so it appeared to the eye as a single pattern.

The simplest way to show the time relationships of this series of pulses was to show the pulses in proper sequence on a line. The line represented a scale of time, corresponding to zero time at one end and $\frac{1}{3720}$ second at the other end. The length of the line corresponded to 269 microseconds in time, or 25 miles in distance or *range*. The line thus made was called a range line. To create such a device we had to have some kind of "pencil" that could draw a straight line and repeat it exactly at the rate of 3720 times a second. While drawing lines at this staggering rate, the pencil would also have to respond to the pulse signals from the radar receiver in order to put some kind of marker on that line for each 5-microsecond signal. The length of the line was important, too. If the 5-microsecond markers were to be spread out enough for each mark to be visible, the marks should be spaced no closer than about twelve to fifteen per inch. And since there could be fifty such marks in 269 microseconds, the line should be about four inches long.

The Cathode Ray "Pencil"

To draw a line four inches long in 269 microseconds, the pencil would have to move at the rate of 15,000 miles an hour. Not only this, but the pencil would have to trace the echo markers whenever they might come, and trace them without losing any writing time. This took a little doing. Fortunately for radar, the cathode ray tube had by that time been developed to the point where it was available for general laboratory use, and it was ideal for a radar indicator. Quite fortuitously, the standard cathode ray tube was five inches in diameter, allowing nicely for a four-inch range line across the center of the screen.

Today the cathode ray tube is well known to us all as the television tube or television screen, though probably very few television spectators know how a cathode ray tube works. But radar came long before television invaded the American home, and it is essential to us here to find out why the cathode ray tube means so much to radar.

Reduced to its simplest terms, a cathode ray tube is a pencil that writes on a special blackboard or screen. The pencil is a stream of electrons from a hot cathode, hence the name *cathode ray*. The screen is a thin layer of tiny *phosphor* crystals attached to the surface of a piece of glass. The stream of electrons is formed, or *focused* to a sharp point, like a pencil point, at the place where it touches the screen. When the electrons in this stream strike the phosphor crystals in the screen, they cause the crystals to glow, which can be seen through the glass as a tiny spot of light at the point of the electron stream. Since the pencil is a stream of electrons flowing from cathode to screen, it can be moved from side to side by either an electric or a magnetic field crossing the path of electron flow (Fig. 36). When such a field is made to change, the point of light on the screen appears to move across the screen. Now this screen differs from an ordinary blackboard in that it constantly erases itself; the light disappears as soon as the electron "pencil" is "turned off." Thus when the pencil moves slowly, the eye sees only a moving spot of light. If it moves very rapidly, then the eye sees a line flash on the screen and disappear. But if the spot moves very

137

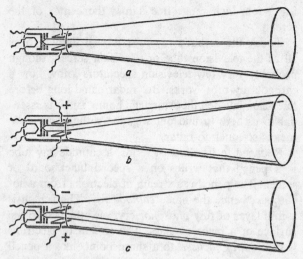

FIG. 36. (a) Cathode ray tube with electron writing beam at center of tube face.

(b) Voltage on deflecting electrodes causes electron beam to write at top of tube face.

(c) Opposite voltage on deflecting electrodes causes electron beam to write at bottom of tube face.

fast and then repeats exactly the same path over and over, the eye sees only a steady line of light. When the line is repeated ten or fifteen times a second, it will appear to flicker, as a movie does when the projector runs too slowly. But at 3720 times a second the eye can see no flicker at all; the line looks perfectly steady.

Since the electrons in the cathode ray "pencil" have almost no mass, they can be moved very fast indeed. The necessary 15,000 miles per hour for that radar in 1936 was quite slow for the electron pencil.

138

In fact, the fast return from the finish of one line to the start for the next line was made at something like a million miles per hour. Thus the pencil would have no trouble tracing out any kind of echo markers while keeping up with the 15,000 mile an hour writing of the range line. The force used to move the pencil, or writing beam, was an electrostatic field between two metallic plates, or deflecting electrodes, so placed that the writing beam normally passed through the center of the space between them. When a voltage, or *potential difference,* was placed on the deflecting electrodes, the writing beam would be deflected or *bent* toward the positive electrode and away from the negative electrode. The greater the potential difference, the greater the degree of bending, therefore the greater the movement of the spot of light on the screen. In order to draw a line on the screen it was necessary to vary the potential difference on the deflecting electrodes.

Since the speed of motion of the spot across the screen is directly proportional to the rate of change of deflecting potential difference, we needed a voltage that changed exactly as we wanted the spot to move. We wanted the spot to start at one side of the screen and move steadily across to the other side of the screen, then very suddenly return to the starting point and repeat the motion over and over. So a voltage generator was built that gave a deflecting potential that changed steadily from one voltage to a second voltage and then suddenly returned to the first voltage. Such a device is called a *sawtooth generator,* since the *wave form,* when plotted out as wave forms usually are illustrated, resembles the teeth of a saw

(Fig. 37). Sawtooth generators were fairly common in 1936, although they had not been in general use very long. The basic method for generating such wave forms was to charge and discharge successively a condenser through resistors—a relatively high resistance giving a large RC time constant was used for one function, to generate the voltage for the line; a relatively low resistance giving a small RC time constant for the other function, to generate the voltage for the fast return from finishing one line to starting the next. Switching from one resistor to the other was done with vacuum tubes, and the switching tube itself usually constituted the lower of the two resistors. The only moving parts in the entire system were electrons. There was no practical mechanical limitation on speeds, and the four-inch range line drawn 3720 times a second was easily obtained.

The next problem was to put an appropriate echo marker on the range line for each signal from the receiver. The most natural mark for this purpose would be a pointer or *pip* standing out from the range line. The range line was made horizontal, with time, or range, reading from left to right. The echo signals were then made pips that stood up vertically. In the cathode ray tube this was accomplished by placing a

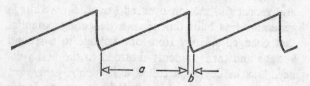

FIG. 37. Wave form of sawtooth generator. Linear sweep voltage is shown at *a*, fast return at *b*. See also Fig. 29.

second pair of deflecting electrodes at right angles with the first pair, so that one pair deflected the writing beam horizontally while the other pair deflected it vertically. The radar receiver then had to amplify the echo signals to over a hundred volts in order to drive the vertical deflection electrodes hard enough to give a full-sized pip with the fast moving beam. You can see why the radar receiver had to have so much more gain than a communication or broadcast receiver, which needed only to provide a few volts output to serve its purpose.

When the cathode ray indicator is used for radar, the position of the transmitted pulse, which also appears on the range line and marks zero range, must be exactly the same every time. The most desirable place is at the extreme left end of the range line. The sawtooth voltage generator must therefore be controlled so as to start the range line exactly when the transmitter starts the pulse. Fortunately, sawtooth generators are easily controlled from externally supplied synchronizing signals. The fast return to the starting voltage results from a trigger action in the switching tube, and when that action is triggered each time by the externally supplied synchronizing signal, the sawtooth voltages are automatically kept in exact step with the synchronizing signal. In radar the synchronizing signal may come from the transmitter itself, or it may come from another source which synchronizes both transmitter and indicator. As I said in Chapter 4, the latter method was used in 1936.

One thing more was required of the indicator. It had not only to present the echoes in proper relative position, but also to show how far away the targets were. At first we put marks on the face of the cathode ray tube, and calculated the number of miles to the target by counting the number of marks from the transmitted pulse to the received echo. This method was not very accurate because the range line had to be carefully positioned relative to the marks, both as to starting point and as to length. Since variations in line voltage or stray magnetic fields would change the position and sometimes the length of the range line, no single measurement of range could be made accurately without first carefully adjusting the range line to the markers on the face of the tube. A better way had to be found. The better way was to generate very short electrical pulses spaced uniformly in time, and then to add these pulses to the receiver output to give tiny indicators on the range line itself. These indicators were synchronized with the range line and appeared attached to the line as parts of the line. They were adjusted until one indicator coincided with the transmitted pulse to denote zero range. When the little indicators were spaced apart ten microseconds in time, they indicated one-mile intervals in space. It was our usual practice to make echo signals point upward from the range line. In order to avoid the possibility of confusion between echo signals and range markers, we made the range markers point downward from the range line. This general type of radar indicator, having a horizontal range line with vertical signal pips, is called an *A scope* (Fig. 38).

Even as early as 1936 it became evident that radar could detect aircraft targets at ranges much greater than twenty-five miles and that target resolution and range precision were not limited to a half mile. Ob-

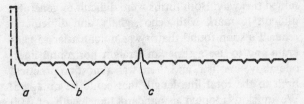

FIG. 38. *A* scope pattern showing transmitted pulse at *a*, range markers, *b*, and echo signal at *c*.

viously, a four-inch range line already was too short to permit indicator readings as accurate at the radar's determinations of range. Larger cathode ray tubes were not available at that time, and when they did become available, the electron pencil point was not so sharp as in smaller tubes, and the writing spot of light consequently became larger as the tube was made larger. This condition resulted in about the same resolution per tube diameter in all sizes and gave no real reading accuracy advantage to the larger tube. Furthermore, since the tube screen was a disc and the range line was a straight line across the center of the circular screen, much of the screen surface was unused.

Many attempts were made to provide a longer range line by using more of the screen surface. The range line was changed to the form of a circle near the outer edge of the screen, with echo signals pointing toward the outer edge or toward the center of the screen. This arrangement gave a line length of about 12 or 13 inches. Another attempted a range line in the form of a spiral making several complete turns from near the outer edge of the screen to near the center of the screen. About 20 inches could be obtained this way. Both forms were difficult to generate, difficult to mark with echo signals, and difficult to read. We soon found that it was much easier to generate and to use a series of straight horizontal lines, one above another, and there was almost no practical limit to the total line length that could be obtained. We quickly adopted a standard line length of 100 microseconds, corresponding to ten miles range, and then used as many lines as needed to get the desired total range of indication. We put range markers at one-mile intervals on the range lines, from which we could estimate to the nearest tenth of a mile between the markers. This was the indicator that was used on the destroyer *Leary* in April 1937.

The Range-Changing Push Button

When we started the design of the XAF radar in 1938, the indicator requirements were re-examined. Ranges beyond twenty-five miles were known to be possible, but since ranges beyond fifty miles were not expected, a transmitter pulse spacing of 538 microseconds was used. It was estimated that a two- or three-line indicator would be adequate. We sought the simplest, most stable, most reliable method of generating such an indicator, and decided upon a rectangular writing motion, in which the electronic pencil would draw the top line from left to right, then drop straight down to the second line and draw right to left, then jump straight up to the top line to begin over again. This system gave a two-line indicator with a twenty-five-mile range on each line. With only a little practice we could read it easily. This turned out to be a most fortunate choice, because this type of indicator was capable of doing some additional tricks that were unforeseen and that later became critically important in the war in the Pacific. All other types of sweep which had been tried would have been unsuitable for the unexpected developments. This is only one more instance of what many would call coincidence, but which I prefer to acknowledge as Divine Guidance. After all, the multiple line indicator used on the U.S.S. *Leary* was already developed and was easily adaptable to two lines, or could have been used with some advantage with three or four, or even five lines. It does not make sense that the subjective compulsion that drove me to abandon it and start over on a totally different approach was only a coincidence with the unforeseen necessity for the new approach.

The first unexpected development was that the XAF frequently got echoes from targets at ranges greater than fifty miles. When this happened, the signal appeared on the indicator just as if it were less than fifty miles away. For example, if an echo was received from a target seventy miles away, it would appear on the indicator as twenty miles away, since the indicator went only to fifty miles before starting over again, and seventy is fifty plus twenty. As time went on, targets were detected at still greater ranges, even in excess of 100 miles. It was thus possible that an echo signal showing at, say thirty miles, might be thirty miles, or eighty miles, or 130 miles, or even some other number times fifty, plus thirty miles. Some way had to be found to determine quickly which was the true range on targets. A very simple method was soon found. A push button was added that enabled the operator to increase the frequency of the synchronizing oscillator by a fixed amount. This arrangement had the effect of shortening the time interval between transmitted pulses and reducing the full-scale range on the indicator. Suppose pushing the button caused an 11 per cent increase in pulse repetition frequency. Then the full-scale range would be reduced from fifty to forty-five miles. A target at twenty miles would then still show at twenty miles when the button was pushed, but a target at seventy miles would jump from twenty ($70 = 50 + 20$) to twenty-five ($70 = 45 + 25$), and a target at 120 miles would jump from twenty ($120 = 2 \times 50 + 20$) to thirty ($120 = 2 \times 45 + 30$).

The next development was the young radar engineers' discovery that the Navy always measured distance in nautical miles, which were longer than the statute miles we were accustomed to using. To accommodate, the synchronizing oscillator frequency was changed to 1640 cycles per second, giving 612.5 microseconds pulse spacing to correspond to fifty nautical miles. What was more natural then than to set the two synchronizing frequencies so that normally the indicator would read in nautical miles, one to fifty, and when the button was pushed in statute miles, one to fifty? This was about the right magnitude of change to give a clear and unmistakable indication of the number of times around the scale each echo had gone, and it required no readjustment of the indicator. Right here is where the new box type of indicator was superior to the former type of multiple line indicator. The synchronizing frequency could be changed at will over wide limits and the indicator followed without readjustment. We could not have done it with a four- or five-line indicator of the type used on the U.S.S. *Leary*.

The choice of nautical miles and statute miles for determining the two frequencies had one very interesting consequence. The change of range indication when the button was pushed happened to be about one-ninth of a full scale. A CXAM radar was installed on the U.S.S. *Yorktown* at Pearl Harbor in the summer of 1940. When she was cruising back to San Diego with her new radar, while yet more than 450 miles from the coast, a series of echoes as of mountains, appeared at about fifteen miles range. Knowing that they were far from any land, the operator pushed the button to determine how far away the targets were. To his amazement and consternation, the echoes stayed right there at fifteen miles. What could it mean? Were they lost and steaming right into some strange rocky island? Had the earth erupted and spewed out mountains in mid ocean? The range was rapidly closing—twelve miles, ten miles, nine miles! A watch was set, but nothing could be seen in or on the water. The operator goggled in awed suspense as the range closed right down to zero—and then the nearest echo just dropped down to the bottom line and appeared at forty-nine miles. What had happened to the radar?

The operator pushed the button again, and now the forty-nine-mile echo moved eight-ninths of the way around the scale. It was now eight times fifty plus forty-nine or 449 miles away! The radar was actually getting echoes from the coastal mountains of California more than 450 miles away. When the echoes were first observed at 15 miles on the indicator, their true distance was 465 nautical miles. That is $9 \times 50 + 15 = 465$. Now, 465 miles on the nautical scale is about 515 miles on the statute scale, so when the button was pushed to change the scale from nautical miles to statute miles, the apparent distance of 515 statute miles was $10 \times 50 + 15$. Since the echoes in both cases would show at 15 miles on the scale, they appeared not to move when the button was pushed. In amazement the operators watched those echoes day and night as they moved around and around the indicator scale, nine times around in all. On the last time around, when pushing the button again gave no range jump to the targets, the operators could go out on the deck and see the mountains of California coming up over the horizon!

Now it was time to raise some embarrassing questions. The radiofrequency used in the CXAM radar was 200 megacycles. At this frequency radio energy does not reflect back to the earth from the ionosphere, as it does at lower frequencies. The energy travels in almost straight lines—or so it was thought at that time. The CXAM on the U.S.S. *Yorktown* was "seeing" mountains over 450 nautical miles away, therefore far below the horizon. How was the radiofrequency energy getting around the earth's curvature so efficiently? Was it bending uniformly by refraction, and if so, what was causing the refraction? Was it reflecting from some hitherto unknown reflecting layer, and if so, what kind of layer was it? The answers to these questions seemed to lie in atmospheric moisture.

Radio waves travel faster in dry air than in moist air. If the air near the earth is moist, and the air high above the earth is dry, and the air is very still, there is likely to be a rather sharp boundary parallel to the earth's surface between the moist air below and the dry air above. Such sharp boundaries are quite familiar to us when the moist air forms a cloud that can be seen floating in clear air. If this boundary is too close to the earth, most radio propagation will be in the dry air above it. If it is too high above the earth, radio waves from below will strike it at so steep an angle that all the energy goes right through the boundary into the dry air. In between these two extremes radio waves from below can strike the boundary at such a small glancing angle that the radio energy is all, or nearly all, reflected or refracted back down again. This behavior is very much like that of light traveling inside a sheet of lucite. When light enters the lucite along one edge, it can travel through the lucite and come out at other edges, but it cannot come out through either face of the lucite sheet because it strikes the surface at such a small angle that it is all reflected back inside the lucite. When a sharp horizontal boundary between moist air below and dry air above exists at a height such that radio waves from below are reflected downward from this boundary, then the space between the surface of the earth and the boundary acts on radio waves as a sheet of lucite does on light waves; the radio waves, trapped in this space, follow it around the earth's curvature for great distances. This condition is called atmospheric ducting.

Such ducting has been found to exist quite frequently over some parts of the earth, especially over the oceans. One may therefore assume that a ducting situation existed when those long ranges were obtained, as if the ship were sailing in an invisible lucite sheet, perhaps a couple of hundred feet thick, fitted neatly to the surface of the Pacific Ocean.

During the war in the Pacific another use was found for the range-changing push button on the CXAM radar. Pushing the button changed the pulsing frequency from 1640 to about 1800 pulses per second. Both of these frequencies are in the audible range. When two ships with CXAM radars pointed their radar beams at each other, and the radar operators put headphones on their radar receivers, each operator could hear the pulse frequency note from the other's radar. The operators then found that by using their push buttons as telegraph keys, they could talk to each other in Morse code. Then they discovered that they could always communicate this way at distances out to 200 miles and beyond, even though there was no ducting. This was another important discovery, although it was not recognized as a new radio propagation mode until several years later when tropospheric forward scatter propagation, as it came to be called, was discovered by the Naval Research Laboratory in 1946.

Had it not been for the high stability of the special indicator developed for the XAF radar, the CXAM radars may never have had the capability of this frequency shift keying. One can never predict the ultimate consequences of decisions which seem at the time to be relatively inconsequential, if not even unnecessary, such as the decision in 1938 to develop a new two-line indicator for the XAF when the multiple-line indicator already existed.

The experience of a task force in the waters around the Aleutian islands made the usefulness of the range-changing push button even more evident. These ships were using other radars which did not have such a push button. While the force was steaming through the darkness one night, with radars on, a group of echoes appeared about sixteen miles in front of the formation. The echoes looked like enemy ships, appeared at about the right range for ships, and showed them to be in open ocean water. The task force closed range and opened fire. But after many rounds of ammunition had been fired that should have been direct hits, none of the target ships sank or caught fire, and none returned the bombardment. The task force ceased fire and continued to close range. When the radars indicated that they were approaching zero range, no other ship could be found there. However, as the task force continued right on through the point of zero range, the same targets showed up again at maximum range, about fifty miles away. This new location coincided with the mountain peaks of a group of islands. Had these radars had a range-changing push button and had the operators used it, they could have known immediately that they were seeing mountains at sixty-six miles instead of ships at sixteen miles, and saved a lot of ammunition, oil, and nerves. This incident is known as the "battle of the pips."

CHAPTER 9

SPECIAL INDICATORS

When the XAF, with its boxlike indicator for measuring range, made the famous cruise on the U.S.S. *New York* in January–February 1939, the system for determining angle of bearing was awkward. The antenna, you will remember, rotated and caused the radar beam to swing past a target. In the traverse the echo signal quickly rose to maximum height and as quickly disappeared. The antenna then had to be stopped and swung back and forth across the target to hunt for the bearing that gave the maximum echo signal. When this was found, the bearing was read from a dial that indicated the direction in which the radar beam was pointing. The accuracy by this method was good enough for general surveillance use, as intended for the XAF, but took too long. When I tried to chart the position of every vessel in a formation of a hundred ships, I spent an hour, and by the time I had located the last ship, the first ones had changed position enough so that they did not fit the chart. As a result, I could never complete a correct

152

chart. It was obvious that a faster method of determining the bearings of many targets was needed.

Measuring the Angle of Bearing

Speed of determining bearing would be increased and the operation simplified if bearing could be indicated right on the cathode ray tube with the range indicator. It would be even better if each echo could be placed on the indicator in a position corresponding to its position relative to the ship carrying the radar. The indicator would then be a chart showing in true relationship the positions of all targets giving echoes. The problem challenged me, and I set out at once to find a way of making such an indicator.

The motions the electronic pencil would have to make were soon determined. It would have to start the range line at the center of the screen, and draw it out toward the edge in a direction corresponding to the direction in which the radar beam was pointed. Then, as the antenna rotated, the range line on the indicator would have to rotate with it, the zero range end remaining stationary at the center while the maximum range end moved in a circle around the edge of the screen. The range line would move on the screen as a spoke moves on a slowly turning wheel. The echo signals, instead of being pips on the range line, would have to be bright spots right in the range line. The bright spots were easy to arrange, since the cathode ray tube has a grid in effect like that in a vacuum tube, which acts as a valve on the electron stream. When the grid is made sufficiently negative relative to the cathode, the electronic pencil is cut off entirely and makes no mark on the screen. If the potential difference between grid and cathode is varied, the electronic pencil can be made to write strongly, weakly, or not at all, and any degree of shading can be obtained. This is the way the picture is produced in a television set. For radar it was only necessary to put the receiver output signals on the cathode ray tube grid (or cathode) to make echo signals brighten the range line instead of deflecting it.

Having determined what motions the electronic pencil would have to make, I next had to find practical means for generating the voltages that would produce those motions. This we found not so easy. Several different methods with electrostatic fields were tried, some of them more successful than others, but all undesirably complex. Then we tried using magnetic fields to produce the motions, and this was successful with considerably simpler electronic circuitry. In magnetic deflection of the cathode ray writing beam, a pair of coils outside the tube neck produces the deflecting field, instead of a pair of metal plates fixed inside the tube. An electric current flowing through the coils will deflect the beam and thus move the spot on the screen. If the current is made to increase uniformly from zero, the spot will move uniformly from the center toward the edge of the tube. A sawtooth current in the coils thus will produce a suitable range line, just as a sawtooth voltage on the electrodes of an electrostatic tube does. But since the deflecting coils are external to the tube, they can be physically rotated around the tube to make the direction of the range line rotate. A servo drive on a rotating pair of deflecting coils, controlled from the rotating antenna, caused the range line to rotate in synchronism with the radar beam so that it always "pointed" in a direction corresponding to the direction of the radar beam.

The Plan Position Indicator

With the proper motions and brightness variations of the electronic pencil achieved, only modification of the screen remained. In all the indicators used before, the A scopes with straight horizontal range lines and vertical signal pips, the screens erased themselves very quickly. But the pattern was repeated so rapidly that the eye could detect no flicker. In this new type of indicator for showing all targets in their true plan position, a whole 360-degree rotation of the antenna was required to generate the indicator pattern once. Since radar antennas were large structures, some of them nearly twenty feet across, they could not be rotated faster than a few revolutions per minute, so it took ten or fifteen seconds to generate one indicator pattern or *chart*. In these circumstances the faint range line could be seen turning around slowly like the spoke on a very slowly turning wheel, and echoes would appear only as short bright flashes of light. It was not possible for the eye or the mind to retain or remember all the flashes in all their correct positions for one complete rotation. Something was needed to hold the light spots on the screen for a longer time so that all the echo spots would remain visible for at least one complete antenna rotation. It happens that the British radar scientists were working on the same problem and made some very clever contributions to its solution. The attempt to use a phosphor in the screen that would continue to glow after being written on—that is, one which would erase itself more slowly—was not successful because such phosphors required too much energy in the electronic pencil to make them glow. Then it was found that two phosphors could be used, one responding to the energy of the electrons in the electronic pencil to give a short, bright flash, and another responding to the flash of light from the first phosphor to give a soft glow for many seconds. This was a big step toward the solution. However, the transitory brilliant flash was so much brighter than the pattern-sustaining soft glow that it was quite disturbing to the eyes when you tried to see the pattern, or chart. Fortunately, the two phosphors gave different colors. The bright flash was blue while the soft glow was orange. When an orange filter was placed in front of the indicator, it let all the orange glow come through, but cut out most of the blue flash. The result was highly successful. This indicator (Fig. 39) was called a *plan position indicator* (PPI), and it is today the most widely used indicator in radar. It is the *radar screen* that has come to symbolize radar in the minds of many people. And like many of the important components of radar, it was developed independently in England and in the U.S.A. when neither country knew of the work in the other country.

The CXAM radars, with their crude method of determining bearing, had one operational advantage which was lost when the PPI was installed. In war-

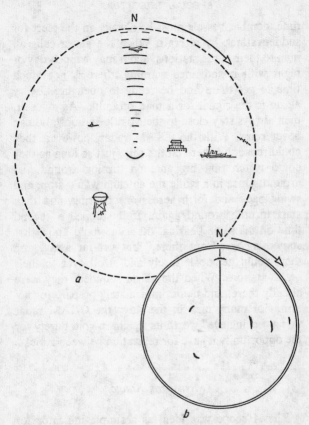

Fig. 39. (a) For plan position indication (PPI) a radar is shown at the center, with its rotating antenna beam just passing the north position and illuminating an aircraft target at long range.

(b) The corresponding indicator is shown with its rotating range line just passing north in synchronism with the antenna beam and "writing" on the screen the aircraft target to the north. The other five targets are shown in the "after glow" of previous rotations of the range line.

time, combat vessels must be always on the alert for sudden attack by aircraft. When the alarm calls all men to their battle stations, and it may happen day or night with no advance warning, there is not much time to get there and be ready to open fire. Every alarm is the signal for a mad scramble. As a result, men always stay close to their battle stations and can never relax. With the CXAM radar, however, they could relax anywhere on the ship, just so long as they could watch that big antenna turning around and around. Once in a while the antenna would stop, and swing back and forth across one bearing, and then start turning around again. If it stopped a second time on the same bearing, the men would know that something was "out there," but yet far away, and they would get up leisurely and stroll over to their battle stations. When the alarm sounded, they were already there, and could immediately prepare for action. For many men in the Navy the CXAM radar was a "seeing eye" worth its weight in gold purely for the opportunity it gave for relaxation between attacks.

Measuring Range

The *A* scope was ideal as a simple indicator for development and early use of radar, and for study of the characteristics of radar echoes. The PPI was ideal for presenting a general radar surveillance picture. But radar has inherently the capability of measuring large distances with greater accuracy than any other method of measuring such distances. Thus it was a welcome solution for the hitherto baffling problem of measuring range for the control of gunfire.

Prior to radar, range to targets for control of gunfire was obtained first with optical rangefinders. At important ranges of interest, such as ten to twenty nautical miles, this method was far too inaccurate, even with the best optical rangefinders. So it was standard practice, after the best estimate with optics had been obtained, to fire one salvo beyond the target and one salvo short of the target, observe the positions of the two sets of splashes where the shells hit the water relative to the target position, and then try to hit the target on the third salvo. This routine was wasteful of both time and ammunition, although it was the most economical method available until radar came along.

With radar it was possible to obtain direct hits with amazing accuracy on the first salvo. However, it required a much more accurate range indicator than the PPI or the ordinary A scope. The first thing that had to be developed was an electrical method of measuring with great precision the time interval from transmitted to received pulses. In fact, if the range were to be known to the nearest twenty-five feet to satisfy the gunners, the time would have to be measured to less than one half of one tenth of a microsecond. And if the target were ten nautical miles away, corresponding to 125 microseconds' time, this meant measuring the time interval with an accuracy of about one part in 5000.

The simplest way to measure such time intervals is to use a circuit that will generate a sharp pulse when it is triggered by another sharp pulse, with a delay that can be controlled between the input trigger

159

and the output pulse. When the transmitted radar pulse is used to trigger the circuit, and the delayed output pulse is made to coincide with the selected echo, accurate determination of the delay time gives accurate indication of range.

There were several circuits capable of this function in 1938, when the work was started. A sawtooth generator is well suited. It is possible to make a sawtooth generator run by itself, without any input pulses to control its period. It is also possible to adjust it so that the sawtooth cycle will not start until it is triggered by an input pulse, but once started it will complete the cycle and return abruptly to the starting point, where it will wait for the next starting pulse. The abrupt return to starting point generates an output pulse. The time delay from starting pulse to output pulse can be controlled over very wide limits by controlling the value of the high resistance in the sawtooth circuit to vary the large RC time constant of the circuit. The delay time is proportional to this RC time constant, and since the capacitance does not change, the delay time is proportional to the resistance value. By using a precision variable resistance for this purpose, one can have a resistance control dial with marks very accurately indicating resistance values, but labeled in terms of range. A more complete description of a delayed pulse generator is given in Chapter 5.

There were several ways of displaying the delayed pulse, which was called the *range marker pulse*. One was to use the range marker pulse to make a bright dot, or a dark dot, in the range line. When the dot appeared on the top of the target pip, it was "on the

160

target" and the range was then read from the dial. Another method was to make the range marker pulse about two or three times as long as the transmitted pulse, and then do two things with it simultaneously. First, add the marker pulse voltage to the range line voltage so as to "write" the range line much faster during the pulse. This "expands" a small part of the range line so that one can read range much more accurately in the expanded portion. Then add the same marker voltage to the vertical deflection electrodes so as to depress or "step down" slightly that portion of the range line that is expanded. This puts a little rectangular "notch" in the range line. In operation the range dial is turned to slide the expanded notch along the range line until the selected target echo drops into the notch. Then the echo is centered in the notch, and the range is read from the dial as before.

The method just described, with either type of presentation, could be made good to about one part in a thousand. In order to get better accuracy another method had to be developed. It consisted basically of a combination of the delayed pulse generator as just described, and multiple-line generator as described in Chapter 7. In the multiple-line generator it is possible to have as many lines as desired, and to make each line represent any desired range interval. It is easy to make the range interval for each line extremely precise, and to make all lines exactly alike. The delayed pulse generator can then be made to cover the range interval of only one line, and yet display the delayed pulse in exactly the same position on all lines.

With this combination it was possible to measure time with any degree of precision you might want. Suppose you wanted to measure time intervals up to 800 microseconds in increments of .02 microsecond, and yet required precision in the range variable resistor of only one part in two hundred. Then each line would be four microseconds long (.02 microsecond × 200 = 4 microseconds), and 200 lines would be used (4 microseconds × 200 = 800 microseconds). To tell which line the echo was on without having to count up to 200 lines, you would use another delayed pulse generator with delay from zero to 800 microseconds, good to 4 microseconds. The pulse from this generator would be used to display the pulse from the other delayed pulse generator so that it would appear on only one line at a time. Each of the two delayed pulse generators would have a range dial, one for coarse adjustment and one for fine adjustment of the range marker. Both dials would be marked with 200 divisions. On the "coarse" dial, each division would correspond to four microseconds in time, or about 2000 feet in range. On the "fine" dial, each division would correspond to two hundredths of a microsecond in time, or about ten feet in range. When you set the dials to determine the range to a selected target, the "coarse" dial would be turned until the range marker appeared on the same line as the selected target, then the "fine" dial would be turned to make the range marker coincide with the selected target. The two dials then could be geared together, controlled with a single knob, and read as you would read a gas meter.

Automatic Tracking

Now we will see how the radar was made to follow the range automatically on any selected target. First it was necessary to *gate* the echo into the automatic circuit (Fig. 40). This was done with a vacuum tube switch that could be turned on and off with lightning speed. The radar receiver output was connected to the automatic range circuit through this switch, or gate, as it was called. The gate was then controlled by a delayed pulse from the precision ranging circuit described above, and made to feed the selected echo into the automatic range circuit and keep all other echoes out. In the automatic circuit were two equal storage condensers and another vacuum tube switch. This second switch operated right in the middle of the gate in such manner as to put all the signal energy from the first half of the gated interval into one storage condenser and all the signal energy from the second half of the gated interval into the other storage condenser. Now it can be seen that if there is an echo

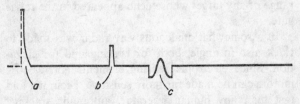

Fig. 40. Precision range indicator showing transmitted pulse at *a*, ungated echo at *b*, and echo gated in center of expanded range notch at *c*.

signal exactly centered in the gate, half of the signal will be stored in each condenser, and the voltages on the two storage condensers will be equal. However, if the range dial is turned a little so that the echo signal is off center, more signal energy will be stored in one condenser than in the other, and there will be a voltage difference between the two condensers. If the range dial is set to too short a range, one condenser will have the higher voltage, and if it is set to too large a range the other condenser will have the higher voltage. Thus, the potential difference between the two condensers is a measure of the error of setting of the range dials for a target in the range gate. The size of the error is indicated by the magnitude of the potential difference, while the sign of the error—that is, whether the dials are set for too close or too far a range—is indicated by the polarity of the potential difference. This potential difference was called the *error signal*. A reversible motor was geared to the range shaft, and the error signal was amplified and connected to the motor in such a way that it drove the motor in the right direction to correct the error in range setting. In this way the radar was made to operate itself in range and to track automatically the range of any target whose echo appeared in the range gate.

In a somewhat analogous way radar was made to track also in angle, both for bearing and for elevation. Since electronic sensing elements and electric motors can be made far more sensitive, accurate, and fast than any human operator, automatic tracking radar gave much better target information to computers for direction of gunfire than was possible with manually operated systems; consequently all radars for control of gunfire, rocket fire, and missile guidance ultimately were made fully automatic.

Interrogation, Friend or Foe

In 1938 it was foreseen that another problem destined to become critical with radar would need to be solved. That was the problem of identifying the targets as friendly or enemy. The first simple experiment was to change the size of the true echo in a rhythmic fashion. Several brass rods cut to a half wavelength of the radar frequency were mounted on a pole, one above another and all in the same vertical plane. When these rods were pointed toward the radar, they gave no reflection, but when they were broadside to the radar they gave a strong reflection. When the pole was set up a couple of miles from the radar and then rotated, an echo signal could be seen from the rods on the pole that would fluctuate up and down rhythmically as the pole was rotated, giving two maxima and two minima for each revolution of the pole. When the XAF radar was taken to sea in 1939, the pole with half-wave rods was taken along and mounted on a destroyer, with a motor to rotate the pole. It was then possible to identify this destroyer among all the other ships as long as the pole was rotating.

This method of causing the signal to fluctuate was much too awkward for use on an airplane, so a similar effect was produced electronically. In place of the variable reflector, a small receiver and transmitter were connected together on the plane so that when a pulse from a radar was received on the plane, it immediately transmitted the pulse back again to the radar. Such a device was called a *transponder*. The pulse sent back by the transponder was always delayed slightly from the radar pulse, and it appeared on the radar screen as another echo very close to the plane. Then just to be sure that it did not appear as another target, a keying device in the transponder continuously keyed it on and off so that on an *A* scope the transponder signal would come and go at a pulsing rate that could be seen with the eye, while on a PPI it appeared as a series of dots close beside the echo from the plane carrying the transponder. With transponders on all friendly planes, observers could quickly identify enemy planes in the radar.

In military operations it was quite undesirable to have one's own aircraft sending out these recognition signals whenever they were in a radar beam. So a separate frequency was used on the radar sets to trigger the transponder, or *Interrogate,* as it is called. Then any airplane could be "interrogated" from the radar by merely pushing an interrogation button long enough to determine whether the proper reply signals were sent back from the airplane. The interrogator on the radar and the transponder on the airplane made a system called IFF, for *Interrogation, Friend* or *Foe.* It soon became "Izzie Friend or Foe?" and, when it failed to work it was called IFFW for "Izzie Friend or Foe, Wazzie?"

IFF as here described was easily copied by the enemy to make his airplane appear "friendly," and so get in to damage his target. There followed a long development of coding methods for IFF signals designed to prevent their use by an enemy, a development which seems to have no end.

CHAPTER 10

EXPLOITS OF RADAR

The U. S. Navy spent a lot of money and time on the development of radar. It spent far more money on procurement of radar apparatus with which to equip its ships and aircraft. What kind of return did our country reap on this investment? What was the real pay-off?

Radar was first developed in America as an instrument for use aboard Naval vessels. Its first operational use on Naval vessels was in January 1939. The original purpose was to give ships early warning against attacking aircraft. This function it performed admirably throughout the war. It not only detected hostile aircraft but tracked them and determined their course and speed. It also gave some information on target altitude and on the number of aircraft in a raid. But no sooner was radar installed aboard ships than other uses developed.

Other Shipboard Uses

For example, the first ship to leave port with a CXAM aboard ran into heavy fog, which threatened to force cancellation of a rendezvous at the end of a three-day run. But the CXAM started "seeing" and tracking other ships in the fog, and giving instructions to the navigator for avoiding collision. After three ships had come within view and glided by at a safe passing distance, as directed by radar, the captain ordered full speed ahead, and sailed confidently through dense fog for three days—and kept his rendezvous. He would not have rested quite so easily had he known that shortly after his order for full speed ahead the radar stopped working and the operators were unaware of the failure. They just didn't see any more ships. How lucky can one get? Perhaps the Lord does take care of those who trust. At any rate, devices were soon developed to indicate at all times how well the radar was working! And navigation through fog and darkness became one of the major functions of radar. This function included "station keeping" in formation with other ships, and detection and tracking of enemy vessels.

It was soon found that radar was useful for directing friendly aircraft to interception of attacking aircraft. Defending aircraft could engage the enemy far from the ships under attack, and frequently destroy the attack, or turn it back, before the enemy closed. This operation was called "fighter direction." Nor was the CXAM a powerful military weapon only in the role of fighter direction. It became a most useful facility for control of air traffic around aircraft carriers. Other radars designed for more precise tracking of single targets were used in the control of approach and landing of aircraft on their carriers. This added capability was critically important, since it freed

Naval aircraft from dependence on good visibility around their carrier for safe return from action.

Another value soon discovered in radar on ships was the ability to keep continuous surveillance of the hundreds of small boats, as well as large craft, in landing operations. Not only could relative positions of all craft be seen at a glance, but the whole land configuration was also displayed on the radar screen. It was almost as if the radar put the spectators in a balloon high over the ship where they could look down on the whole operation and see everything going on.

Later in the war radars with a wavelength of only a few centimeters became available. These were called *microwave* radars. Capable of producing very sharp beams with relatively small antennas, they were used for direction of gunfire. Against other ships radar was highly successful, making direct hits on the first salvo a commonplace occurrence. Against shore targets it was somewhat degraded by the many confusing echoes from objects other than the desired targets. It was sometimes possible to overcome such confusion, at least partially, by getting a transponder ashore for a beacon. If a shore party could place a beacon in a location well known relative to the target, the radar on ship could then use that beacon as a known reference and as an off-set point of aim to hit the desired target. Radar control of gunfire was used extensively against aircraft, although in this application the capabilities of radar were taxed to the limit of the state of the art at the time. In fact, though radar was exceedingly useful in antiaircraft fire control during World War II, it never became fully adequate to the task. The limitations have largely been overcome since the war, but that is a big story in itself. Suffice it to say in this regard that postwar developments in radar are not significantly less than prewar developments.

Truly the addition of radar to the Navy's ships added immeasurably to their capability. Not only did it provide, in fog, smoke, and darkness as well as in daylight, early warning against aircraft attack, but it also made possible safe navigation, station keeping, and surveillance of our own forces, detection and tracking of enemy vessels, fighter direction, air traffic control, homing, approach and landing of aircraft on carriers, surveillance of landing operations, and direction of gunfire against ships, shore targets, and aircraft. It enabled a few destroyers, unaided and singlehanded, to ambush and destroy whole fleets of cruisers and battleships, and themselves escape unscratched. Even if radar had had no other use than on the ships of the U. S. Navy, it could truly be called the miracle weapon of World War II.

Airborne Radar

Radar, however, did have other uses. When put on aircraft, it performed miracles as spectacular as those performed on ships. The story of the Battle of Britain has been told many times, as a tribute to British radar as well as to the indomitable Royal Air Force pilot. As American radar was developed by the U. S. Navy and thus gave to the U. S. Navy the best shipborne radar in the world, so British radar was developed by the Royal Air Force and thus gave England an early lead in airborne radar. When American radar took to the air, it used the British airborne receiver and indicator, but a new transmitter developed by the U. S. Naval Research Laboratory. There were good reasons for the new transmitter. British airborne radar then used a 200 mc transmitter with a radically new transmitter tube not well adapted to higher frequencies. But at 200 mcs the necessary radar beam antennas were so large they were quite awkward on an airplane. It was necessary to reduce the antenna size drastically to avoid compromising the performance of our aircraft, and the only way to do that was to use a much higher frequency.

At that time the development had just been completed on a phenomenal new radar tube by the same San Bruno tube company that had produced the tubes for the XAF and CXAM radars. This new tube, called the 15-E, was a deceptively simple looking triode, about two inches in diameter and two and a half inches long, but it was the result of many months of intensive research in electrode materials and electrode treating. It solved the problems of phenomenally high cathode emission combined with fantastically low grid emission in the absence of high anode temperatures to keep the electrodes clean. Six of these tiny tubes in the Naval Research Laboratory ring oscillator gave pulse powers of 60 kilowatts at 500 mcs, and 50 kw at 600 mcs. It was found, however, that the 20 kw that could be obtained from two tubes was adequate for airborne radar at 500 mcs, so the American airborne radar type ASB was built with a British-type receiver and indicator, and an NRL-type two-tube 15-E 500 mc, 20 kw pulse transmitter. This set was so successful that several companies were tooled to produce it, and 26,000 sets were built for the U. S. Navy. It was the set that fought the war from the air in the Pacific.

Airborne radar performed several functions as important to military aircraft as seeing is important to man. Originally it was intended to detect and track other aircraft in the pursuit and destruction of attacking bombers. It was in this function, aided by early warning and fighter direction from ground radars, that it contributed so heavily to driving off the German attacks in the Battle of Britain. The story is told of an RAF night fighter pilot whose airplane, loaded and slowed down as it was by the big radar antenna, was unable to overtake the bomber he was pursuing in the dark by radar. Having got on the bomber's trail over the English Channel, he followed it clear in to London, where it dropped its bombs and headed back for home. When they reached the Channel again, the Nazi bomber pilot, feeling safe at last, eased back on the throttle a bit to save his engines and have gas enough to get home. That was his last mistake.

When aircraft started carrying radar sets, the pilots soon discovered that the radar could see ships on the ocean at great distances. This capability so greatly increased the power of aircraft to search the oceans for ships that submarines were driven below and deprived of their freedom to cruise on the surface for charging batteries and enjoying fresh air, and all ships lost the tremendous advantage of cover of darkness and fog for concealing their movements. Not only that, aircraft were soon able to use radar to direct their attack on ships at night, and ships that were not equipped with radar to protect themselves became easy prey to the radar-equipped torpedo plane.

Whether attacking enemy ships or seeking the haven of mother carrier, it was all the same to radar, day or night, fog or bright. The most welcome sight to a pilot returning from his mission and running low on fuel is the pip on his radar screen when he finally picks up his own carrier and can "home in" by radar.

The British-type airborne radar indicator was different from the A scope and the PPI that have been described. This radar used two antennas, both pointing forward but one diverted slightly to the right and the other slightly to the left. The radar was then switched rapidly back and forth between the two antennas. The range line on the indicator was made vertical, with zero range at the bottom and maximum range at the top. The echo pips were then pointed horizontally away from the range line, those from the right-looking antenna to the right and those from the left-looking antenna to the left. When a target was directly ahead of the aircraft, both antennas saw it equally well, and the right and left echoes were equal on the indicator. If the target was a little off to one side of directly ahead, it would be seen better by the antenna on that side, and poorer by the antenna on the other side; the echo that appeared on the indicator would be larger on that side of the range line and smaller on the other side. Homing on a particular target was then accomplished by so steering the airplane that the range line stayed centered in the double echo pip from the target.

Searching the oceans for ships and submarines, attacking enemy ships, and homing on carriers were functions well performed by the 500 mc ASB radars. For other functions, such as navigation over land, a PPI was needed, with a high resolution radar. High resolution required a short pulse and a sharp or narrow radar beam. As we saw in Chapter 1, the sharpness of the radar beam depends on the size of the antenna in wavelengths of the radar frequency. Airborne antennas had to be small; therefore, sharp beams required the use of microwaves. Great Britain, in the early development of microwave radar, had introduced the cavity magnetron, a microwave transmitting tube capable of producing very high power pulses. The Radiation Laboratory of the Massachusetts Institute of Technology, under contract with the National Defense Research Committee, combined British microwave radar designs, including the cavity magnetron, with U.S. radar designs, including the duplexer, and worked with American industry to develop and produce microwave radar in large quantities for military use. When installed on aircraft with the PPI, this microwave radar produced beautifully clear and detailed "charts" of the ground underneath. Radar waves striking water and paved roads reflected forward with almost no scattering back to the radar. Water and roads therefore appeared black on the screen. On land, however, all structures, trees, hills, and even the roughness of the ground itself reflected radar waves back to the radar receiver, and land areas appeared bright with many reflecting objects. It was easy to see rivers, lakes, ocean areas, and roads as dark lines and areas, and telephone and power lines, railroads, and fences as light lines. Mountains and the large buildings of cities and towns stood out brightly over all surrounding areas. With prior knowledge of the geography and topography being overflown, aircraft could navigate over land by radar, even when the land was entirely obscured by clouds or darkness. This capability enabled bombers to locate and bomb their targets independently of weather, darkness, and camouflage.

The story has been told many times how radar-equipped aircraft drove the submarines from the Atlantic Ocean in World War II. At first, meter wave radars, the British 200 mc ASV and the American 500 mc ASB, were highly successful. Then the submarines started carrying their own listening receivers, and when they heard the pulse signals from the searching aircraft, they could dive before the aircraft got close enough to attack. When the aircraft got microwave radar, however, they approached the submarines undetected, because the listening receivers on the submarines could not be tuned to the microwave frequencies. Dependent as those submarines were on surface operation for cruising speed, battery charging, and fresh air maintenance, they became helpless when denied use of the surface of the sea. Snorkeling was not a solution, for even the snorkel could be detected and homed on by the radar. Had it not been for airborne radar, and especially microwave radar, the German submarines would have succeeded in destroying all Allied shipping, and the outcome of the war would almost certainly have been reversed.

Airborne radar, in freeing aircraft from the crippling limitations of darkness, clouds, and fog won the Battle of Britain, drove the submarines from the oceans, and turned Allied defeat into victory on land in Europe. The contribution of airborne radar to the defense of our country has been inestimably great.

Ground-Based Radar

The story has often been told of radar's part in the surprise attack on Pearl Harbor on December 7, 1941. The Japanese aircraft were detected by U. S. Signal Corps-developed ground-based surveillance radar in ample time to mount a counterattack, which would at least have blunted, if not repulsed, the attack, and conceivably could have sunk the enemy carriers. The warning was given by the radar operator, but ignored by his command. Too often the account of wartime ground-based radar has emphasized this fascinating but highly embarrassing incident, making more obscure the revolutionary achievements of ground-based radar in other areas. The early warning and fighter direction services of the first radars in battle, the coastal chain stations of Great Britain, constituted one of the indispensable elements in the defense of Britain.

There may have been another turning point in 1944 when the buzz bomb, launched from the shores of France, began to appear over the English Channel in large numbers. I say *may* have been, because another ground-based radar development met the challenge, and destroyed the threat before the emergency demonstrated turning point dimensions.

In its application of microwave radar to military

use the Radiation Laboratory of M.I.T. developed a precision automatic tracking radar for Army use, which became the famous SCR-584. Teamed with the almost equally famous M-1 computer for anti-aircraft gunfire direction, the SCR-584 provided accuracy of gunfire control far surpassing all its predecessors. On manned aircraft targets, capable of evasive maneuvers, such accuracy of fire control was wasted, since the target could change course and speed after guns were fired but before the projectiles could reach the predicted point of impact with the target, thus failing to keep the rendezvous with death. The pilotless buzz bombs, however, held to a course and speed both steady and true, and as soon as these quantities were determined by the tracking radar, future positions of the target could be predicted with great accuracy. Before introduction of the SCR-584 –M-1 combination, many thousands of rounds of ammunition were fired for each buzz bomb shot down. With the new system, designed and built by the Radiation Laboratory of M.I.T. and American industry, the average number of rounds fired for target destroyed fell to approximately 50. Early detection and location by the coastal chain stations, precision tracking with the SCR-584, accurate position prediction by the M-1, and the precise calibration of the British antiaircraft guns made a devastating combination. Once it started "clicking," few buzz bombs reached the western shores of the English Channel.

It would be hard to exaggerate the contribution of ground-based radar to the defense of England. Without the early warning and fighter direction services of the coastal chain stations in 1940 and 1944, and without the fantastically accurate tracking of buzz bombs by the SCR-584, the Battle of Britain could very well have been lost, and with it, the war. Conversely, it is the German claim that the Allied invasion of Europe could not have been successful had not the German antiaircraft radars been completely nullified by providentially successful Allied jamming. From such potency in war there should be some residual value for peacetime operations. These merit at least a brief review before closing our story of the origin of radar.

Radar in Industry

When, in 1936, the Naval Research Laboratory demonstrated to some of the engineers and executives of the Bell Telephone Laboratories the capabilities of radar, Mr. Nelson of the Bell Telephone Laboratories said that private industry never would have undertaken the development of radar because it promised so little in commercial return. Where does that prophecy stand now, twenty-five years later? Let us ignore the twenty billion dollars spent on military radar in World War II, and consider only the peacetime uses that have emerged. The first to appear, naturally, were peacetime applications in functions for which radar had wartime use. One such function is navigation of ships through fog and in darkness. It is difficult to estimate the significance of all the shipping on inland waterways—the Great Lakes, the great rivers, the canals, and all the great harbors of the world, with ocean-going ships, coal, oil, and ore barges, river steamers, ferries, tugs, and pleasure craft. It is even more difficult to comprehend the magnitude of the devitalizing effects of fog on this commerce throughout the world. Radar on private ships has set them free from the prison of fog and saved untold numbers of lives and wealth of cargoes. Radar on the shores around busy harbors also contributes much to the safe and easy flow of water traffic in all conditions of visibility.

Another such application is navigation of aircraft to avoid rough weather in flight. Air passengers owe much of their comfort and safety to the airborne radar which displays to the pilot the weather map of storm clouds and air turbulence for a hundred miles around.

Ground-based radar for surveillance of air traffic, in cross-country flights, and in the vicinity of airports, is another important conversion of a wartime operation to a peacetime use. Instead of guiding warplanes in a holding pattern or bringing them in to land on a carrier, airports direct into holding patterns or bring in to the proper runways the huge modern liners of the air with their hundreds of passengers. Not only that, but once on the ground, the airplanes, along with all other vehicles, are kept in constant surveillance and control by airport taxi radar that can even see a man walking, be he in sunshine, or fog, or the blackness of night.

Radar in Science

Another use of radar had a small start in war but has been greatly expanded in peacetime use. That is the use of radar for weather surveillance.* Rainfall is easily seen by radar, and weather fronts and hurricanes are usually marked by heavy rainfall. Radar with its PPI has become a most useful tool in mapping out weather fronts and hurricanes over large areas, especially over the oceans, where it is difficult to maintain many weather stations.

Perhaps the most exciting peacetime use of radar is in scientific research. It is possible with radars especially designed as research instruments to get echoes from the moon and nearby planets of the solar system. With radar, the Naval Research Laboratory discovered in 1953 that the moon, contrary to expectation, can be used effectively as a reflector for radio communication, over a very large part of the radiofrequency spectrum. A powerful transmitter may direct a radio communication signal to the moon, and that signal can be received and understood at any point on the earth that can see the moon. The moon is now being used for that purpose with great success.

From study of radar echoes from the moon, much is learned about propagation of electromagnetic energy through the earth's atmosphere, the ionosphere,

* See *Radar Observes the Weather* by Louis J. Battan, Science Study Series, Doubleday & Company, Garden City, 1962.

and the space between earth and moon. Precision radar measures with great accuracy the distance to the moon, and the rate of change of that distance with time. Such measurements made from several widely spaced points on the earth's surface can tell us much about the shape of the earth, the position of the earth's center of mass, and the precise relative position of the earth's continents and islands.

Radar echoes from other planets will some day give information about those planets which can be obtained in no other way, leading to a better understanding of our solar system. Likewise radar echoes from the sun, when they are achieved, will supplement the vast amount of information about the sun, its atmosphere, and its processes now being obtained by balloon and rocket astronomy and other ingenious means.

Great as were the consequences of the use of radar in World War II, its ever expanding applications to the processes of peace promise to overtake and surpass its military importance. From enabling ships of the sea and of the air to pass safely in the night to advancing the frontiers of our knowledge of the universe, radar has far exceeded its promises.

RADAR CHRONOLOGY

Scientific Foundation of Radar

1832 Faraday (U.K.) postulated the electromagnetic field.

1873 Maxwell (U.K.), working from Faraday's hypothesis, predicted mathematically the existence and behavior of radio waves.

1879 Hughes (U.K.) generated them over a distance of 100 yards.

1886 Heinrich Hertz (Germany) conclusively demonstrated radio waves, including reflection, refraction, direction finding.

1924 Appleton and Barnet (U.K.) used radio wave phase velocity to measure the difference in length of two propagation paths.

1925 Breit, Tuve, and Taylor (U.S.) used radio wave group velocity to measure the difference in length of two propagation paths. Interference due to aircraft flying near equipment noted, considered only as a nuisance.

1933 British Post Office Engineers observed disturbance to short-wave radio by passing airplane. Bell Telephone Laboratories observed and explained it. Both considered it a nuisance.

Pre-Radar Technology

1897 Braun (Germany) devised cathode ray tube.

1900 Nikola Tesla (Yugoslavia) suggested use of electromagnetic waves to determine relative position, speed, and course of a moving object.

1903 Huelsmeyer (Germany) detected radio waves reflected from a ship and applied for a patent for a anticollision device based on c.w. radio direction finding.

1906 DeForrest (U.S.) invented the triode vacuum tube.

1913 DeForrest and Armstrong (U.S.) independently invented the regenerative circuit.

1919 Armstrong (U.S.) invented the superheterodyne receiver.

1921 Hull (U.S.) of General Electric invented magnetron tube.

1922 June   Marconi (Italy) again suggested use of radio for obstacle detection.

1923 July   Loewy (Austria) filed U.S. patent application for detection of objects by a radio version of the Fizeau wheel principle. Since range indication was ambiguous and one target would jam it for all other targets, it had little operational advantage over Huelsmeyer.

Significant Events in the Origin of Radar

1922 Sept.   Taylor and Young (U.S.) observed interruption of high frequency radio communication by ship passing between transmitter and receiver. Also observed "beats" produced by large objects moving in the propagation field.

1922	Sept.	Taylor and Young (U.S.) proposed use of radio signal interruption phenomenon for detecting ships in darkness and fog.
1930	June	Hyland (U.S.), colleague of Taylor and Young, observed c.w. radio reflection from aircraft in the form of "beats."
1930	Nov.	Taylor, Young, and Hyland (U.S.) proposed radio "beat" method of detection of aircraft and ships.
1931	Jan.	Project assigned by Navy Bureau of Engineering to U. S. Naval Research Laboratory, "Detection of Enemy Vessels and Aircraft by Radio."
1934	Mar. 14	Young and Page (U.S.), under supervision of Taylor, started the development of pulsed radar.
1934	Dec.	Young and Page (U.S.): first radar echoes. Saturation signal on single-seat "wood and fabric" airplane at 1 mile.
1935	Feb.	Watson-Watt (U.K.) proposed radar when asked to devise a "death-ray" proposal.
1935	June	Watson-Watt (U.K.): first radar echoes in England, 15 miles on flying boat.
1935	July	U. S. Army Signal Corps started work on pulsed radar.
1936	Feb.	Watson-Watt (U.K.) proposed airborne radar and work commenced.
1936	Mar.	Watson-Watt (U.K.) tracked aircraft beyond 80 miles.

1936 April   Page and Guthrie (U.S.), with second experimental radar set, obtained excellent echoes to the 25-mile maximum range of indicator scale.

1936 July   Varela (U.S.) completed and successfully operated first radar on 200 mcs.

1936 July   Young and Page (U.S.): first radar duplexer.

1936 Fall   Page (U.S.) developed precision range indicator.

1937 April   Destroyer U.S.S. *Leary* successfully tested sea-going radar.

1937 April   British Government reached decision to cover east and south coasts of England and Thames Estuary with a radar detection network.

1937 May   First U. S. Army Signal Corps demonstration of radar.

1937 Aug.   Page (U.S.): first multi-tube ring oscillator.

1938 Feb.   High-power ring oscillator, later used in radar models XAF and CXAM. 15 kw pulse power at 200 mc with six tubes.

1938 Dec.   Battleship U.S.S. *New York* equipped with radar.

1939   XAF radar operated on U.S.S. *New York* detected navigation buoys at 4 nautical miles; surface ships at 8 to 15 nautical miles; birds at 5½ nautical miles; 14-inch shells in flight and fall-of-shot splashes at 7 nautical miles; aircraft at 100 nautical miles; mountains at 70 nautical miles.

1940	Aug. & Sept.	Tizard Committee (U.K.) came to U.S. to make full disclosure and share war materiel, techniques, and devices; brought an improved magnetron which made microwave radar practical and took back to England the highly successful radar duplexer.
1940	Oct.	Radiation Laboratory of M.I.T. organized under contract with NDRC. In following years, combined American and British radar contributions to develop microwave radar.

INDEX

SCIENCE STUDY SERIES

DATE DUE